A Building Craft 'Foundation'

NVQ: Common Core

The NVQ Construction Series titles are:

A BUILDING CRAFT FOUNDATION by Peter Brett
(covers the five common core units)

CARPENTRY AND JOINERY by Peter Brett
(covers the Site Carpentry units)

BENCH JOINERY by Peter Brett
(covers the Bench Joinery units)

PAINTING AND DECORATING
(covers the Painting and Decorating units)

PLASTERING
(covers the Plastering units)

BRICKLAYING by W. G. Nash
(covers the Bricklaying units)

A Building Craft 'Foundation'

NVQ: COMMON CORE

Peter Brett

BROOKLYN COLLEGE, BIRMINGHAM

Stanley Thornes (Publishers) Ltd

First published in 1991 by:
Stanley Thornes (Publishers) Ltd
Ellenborough House
Wellington Street
CHELTENHAM GL50 1YW
England

96 97 98 99 00 / 10 9 8 7 6 5 4 3

British Library Cataloguing in Publication Data

Brett, Peter
A building craft foundation: NVQ: common core.
—(Building craft series)
I. Title II. Series
690

ISBN 0–7487 1114–7

Typeset by Tech-Set Ltd, Tyne & Wear
Printed and bound in Great Britain at The Bath Press, Bath

Contents

Acknowledgements

The author wishes to thank the following:

The official forms included in this package are reproduced with the permission of the Controller of Her Majesty's Stationery Office who reserve Crown Copyright.

My sincere thanks go to my colleagues, in particular Ken Trethowan, for their assistance and encouragement.

Word-square searches were kindly produced by James Brett.

This building craft series is dedicated to Shalimar.

National vocational qualifications – NVQs

The work of a skilled person in the construction industry can be divided into various tasks, e.g. build a brick wall, paint a ceiling, hang a door, etc. These tasks along with many others are called **Units of Competence**. They can be considered as a 'menu' for selection by yourself on a 'pick and mix' basis according to your requirements.

Traditional barriers to gaining a qualification such as age, length of training, mode of training, how and where skills are acquired, have been removed. You may train for NVQs in any order as, when and where you want.

Credits for Units of Competence which can be accumulated over any period of time, may be built into an NVQ award at three levels:

NVQ Level I	Introduction to industry, a 'foundation' common core plus occupational basic skills, e.g. wood occupations, trowel occupations etc.
NVQ Level II	A subset of Units of Competence in a recognisable work role, e.g. bench joinery, site carpentry, bricklaying, etc.
NVQ Level III	A set number of relevant Units of Competence in a chosen occupational area of work, including supervisory and assessment studies, e.g. carpenter and joiner, bricklayer, etc.

NVQ qualifications in construction are jointly awarded by City and Guilds of London Institute (CGLI) and Construction Industry Training Board (CITB).

Prior achievement

It is not always necessary to undertake training for every Unit of Competence as colleges and other accredited centres will in future be able to undertake **Accreditation of Prior Learning/Achievement (APL/A)**. Through this process it is possible to gain credits for Units of Competence which have either formed part of another course you have studied, or tasks you have previously carried out in industry.

You will need to produce evidence of the competence from past performance. This would then be taken into account when determining your training/accreditation programme and for the award of a qualification.

The advantages of this process are:

- increased motivation of trainees because there is no duplication of training previously carried out
- easier access to qualifications for experienced and mature trainees who have not had the opportunity to demonstrate their competences earlier.

A guide for lecturers, instructors and supervisors ('tutors')

An NVQ programme is unit based, it needs to be flexible so that an employer or individual can specify a training and accreditation programme specifically to their requirements. Set length courses will become a thing of the past and a 'roll-on/roll-off' system of independent competency units, packaged according to employer or individual needs will come to the fore. Each unit is intended to be entirely free-standing with no prescribed order of attainment, time duration or start time. Therefore trainees with widely differing abilities and undertaking varying units, will have to be accommodated by the 'tutor'.

A trainee-centred learning approach using learning packages supported by tutor reinforcement and guidance is the ideal answer. It enables a flexible learning programme which caters for self selection, individual progression, mixed ability and 'roll-on/roll-off' programmes.

Using this method the trainees are made responsible for their own learning, which is task orientated. The tutor's role changes to one of a facilitator, counsellor and assessor.

A Building Craft 'Foundation' and the follow on Building Craft Competence Series of craft/level specific packages provides a resource base for the implementation of NVQ Building Craft programmes within your training environment. In addition to these packages a Tutor's Guide is available which gives advice on learning strategies, provides answers to the trainee tasks undertaken in the *'Foundation'* and also contains numerous photocopier-ready worksheets for further trainee activity.

Introduction

The learning package which you are about to start is a building craft 'foundation'. It covers the NVQ Construction common core for **all trainees**, and is intended as an introduction to the industry. Once successfully completed it forms part of an NVQ occupational award.

All units should be undertaken in their entirety by the new entrant to the industry to provide a foundation on which other Units of Competence can be built.

As an alternative, persons with prior achievement may choose to undertake individual foundation units as refreshers, to support other level Units of Competence according to their needs.

How to use this package

This is a self-study package designed to be supported by:
- tutor reinforcement and guidance
- group discussion
- films, slides and videos.

You should read/work through each section of a unit, one at a time as required. Discuss its content with your group, tutor, or friends wherever possible. Attempt to answer the *Questions for you* in that section. Progressively read through all the sections, discussing them and answering the questions as you go.

This process is intended to aid learning and enable you to evaluate your understanding of the particular section and to check your progress through the units and entire package. Where you are unable to answer a question, further reading and discussion of the section is required.

Throughout this learning package 'Harry' the general foreman and his thoughts will prompt you to undertake an activity or task.

The *Questions for you* in this package are either multiple choice or short answer.

Multiple-choice questions consist of a statement or question followed by four possible answers. Only **one** answer is correct, the others are distractors. Your response is recorded by filling in the line under the appropriate letter.

Example

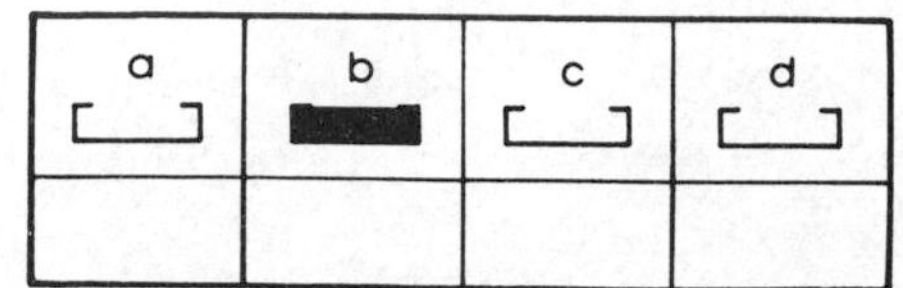

This indicates that you have selected (b) as the answer.

If after consideration you want to change your mind, fill in the box under your first answer and then fill in the line under the new letter.

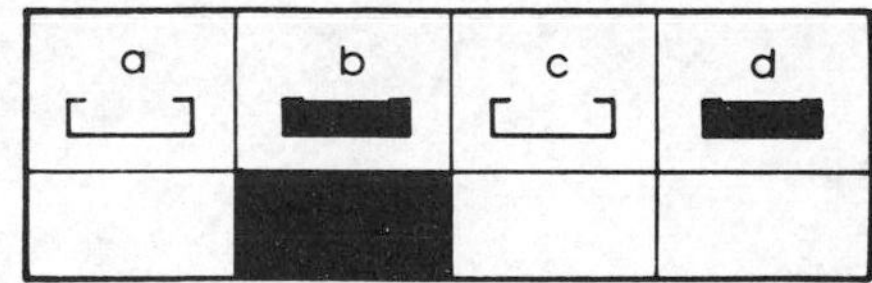

This changes the answer from (b) to (d).

Short-answer questions consist of a task to which a short written answer is required. The length will vary depending on the 'doing' word in the task, **Name** or **List** normally require one or two words for each item, **State**, **Define**, **Describe** or **Explain** will require a short sentence. In certain cases a labelled sketch may be all that is required.

Example

Name the architect's on-site representative.

Typical answer: The clerk of works.

Example

Define the term 'the building team'.

Typical answer: The team of professionals who work together to produce the required building or structure. Consists of the following parties: client, architect, quantity surveyor, specialist engineers, clerk of works, local authority health and safety inspector, building contractor, sub-contractors and material suppliers.

Example

Make a sketch to show the difference in size between a brick and a block.

Typical answer:

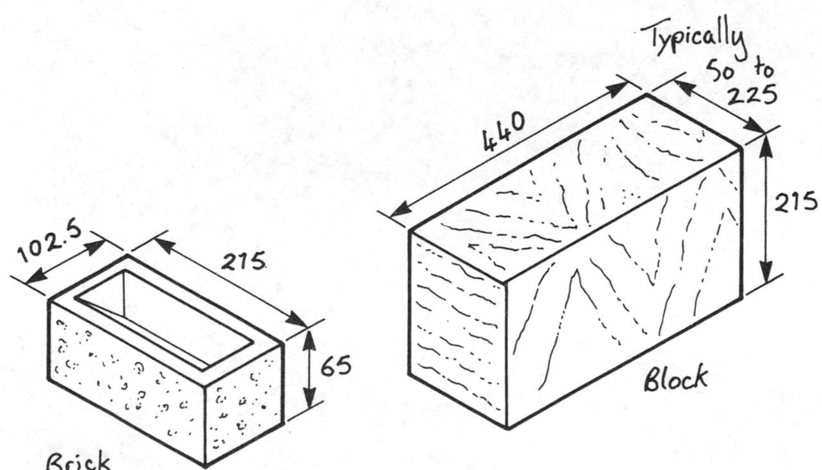

In addition this package also contains *Learning tasks*. Follow the instructions given with each exercise. They are intended to reinforce the work undertaken in this package. They give you the opportunity to use your newly acquired awareness and skills.

In common with NVQ knowledge and understanding assessments, the learning exercises in this package may be attempted orally. You can simply tell someone your answer, point to a diagram, indicate a part in a learning pack or textbook, or make sketches, etc.

1 The construction industry

Introduction to the construction industry

The 'construction industry' in its widest sense covers the following **four** main areas of work. They all work to the same purpose, that is the provision of shelter and other services to the population as a whole.

Building

This is the construction, maintenance and adaptation of buildings ranging from office blocks, industrial complexes and shopping centres to schools, hospitals, recreation centres and homes. Included in this area are the specialist builders who concentrate on the provision of one skill, e.g. glazing, cladding, tiling and roofing, etc.

Civil engineering

This is the construction and maintenance of public works such as roads, railways, bridges, airports, docks, sewers, etc.

Mechanical engineering

This is the installation, commissioning and maintenance of lifts, escalators and heating, ventilation, refrigeration, sprinkler and plumbing systems, etc.

Electrical engineering

This is the installation, commissioning and maintenance of various electrical and electronic devices.

Range of work

Contained within these four main work areas are a variety of specific job functions and careers giving employment to well over a million people, plus one in five of Britain's self-employed workers. These are men and women working in offices and sites up and down the country. Either directly or indirectly approximately one in ten of the working population is involved in construction.

The value of the work carried out in the UK annually is approximately £35 000 million, accounting for about 10 per cent of the country's gross national product. Examples of this work can be seen almost everywhere. They range from basic housing repairs through to multi-million-pound developments such as airports, motorways, bridges, tunnels, business parks (factories and offices) and new town developments.

About 60 per cent of the annual total can be attributed to new work and 40 per cent to maintenance, refurbishment and renovation work. Of this about 37 per cent is spent on housing, with the remaining 63 per cent being spent on other works.

New: a building that has just been built.

Maintenance: the **repairs** undertaken to a building and its services in order to keep it at an acceptable standard so that it may fulfill its function.

Refurbishment: to bring an existing building up to standard, or make it suitable for a new use by **renovation**.

Restoration: to bring an existing building back to its original condition.

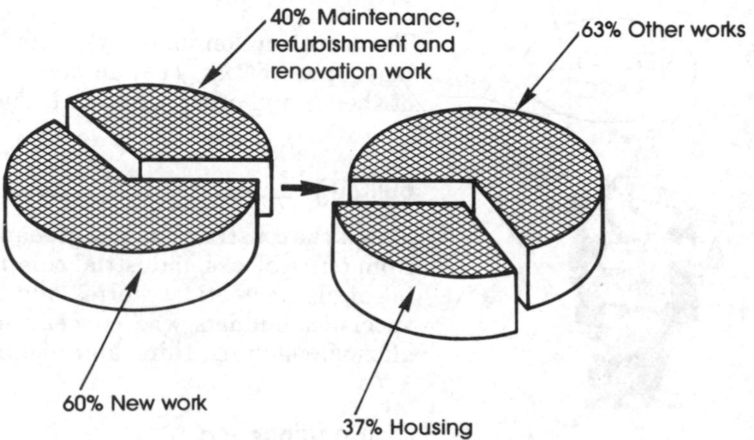

Although a major employer, the industry is possibly one of the most fragmented. Firms vary widely in size, from the small-scale local builder employing perhaps two or three people, to the international companies employing thousands. Of the total workforce, the private sector contractors (privately owned firms who undertake building work in order to make a profit) account for about 88 per cent of those employed. The remaining 12 per cent are employed by the building departments of public sector authorities (council building departments for housing, education and hospitals, etc, often termed direct or public works departments), a large proportion of whose work is concerned with repairs, maintenance and restoration.

Statistics show there are around 75 000 contracting firms who employ two or more people, and whilst there are a number of very large firms the vast majority of firms in the industry (92 per cent) employ fewer than 25 people.

Firms are classified by size into three groups according to the number of employees employed:

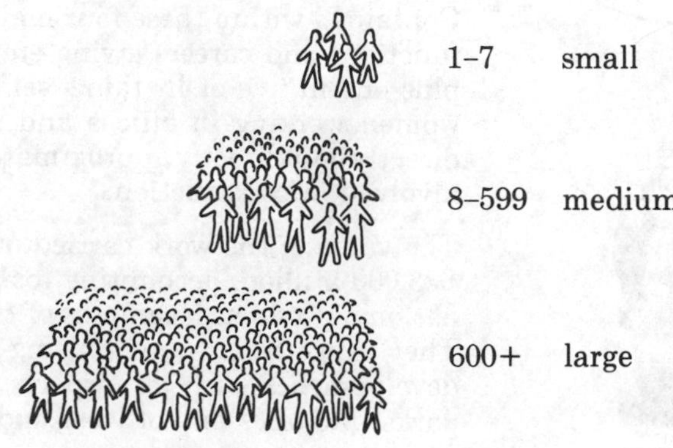

1–7 small

8–599 medium

600+ large

Careers

The construction industry offers employment in four distinct career areas: professional, technician, building crafts, building operatives.

Professional

These graduate-entry positions include the following:

Architect – designs and supervises the construction of buildings.

Engineer – can be either a civil engineer (concerned with roads and railways, etc.), structural engineer (concerned with the structural aspects of a building's design) or a service engineer who plans building-service systems.

Surveyor – can be either a land surveyor (who determines positions for buildings, roads and bridges, etc.), a building surveyor (who is concerned with the administration of maintenance and adaptation works as well as new buildings), a quantity surveyor (who measures and describes building works using information contained on architects' drawings; in addition they also prepare valuations of works in progress).

Technician

This is the link level in the industry between the professional and craft areas. The main job functions of technicians are as follows:

Architectural technician – involved with the interpretation and presentation of the architect's design information, into a form suitable for use by the builder.

Building technician – involved with the estimating, purchasing, site surveying, site management and documentation of building works.

Building surveying technician – may specialize in building maintenance, building control or structural surveys, etc.

Quantity surveying technician – calculates costs and payments for building works.

Building crafts

The building crafts involve the skilled operatives who work with specific materials and actually undertake the physical tasks of constructing a building. The main examples are as follows:

Bricklayer – works with bricks and mortar to construct all types of walling, also concerned with maintenance and adaptation of existing works.

Carpenter and/or joiner – works with timber, other allied materials, metal/plastic items and ironmongery. They make, fix and repair all timber components in buildings. Carpenters work on building sites, whereas joiners work mainly in a workshop at the bench.

Electrician – works with metals, plastics, wire and cables, and installs and maintains electrical systems.

Formworker – works with timber, metal and plastic, etc. to produce a structure that supports and shapes wet concrete until it has become self-supporting.

Painter and decorator – works with paint, paper, fabrics and fillers, to decorate or re-decorate new and existing works; they sometimes glaze windows and carry out sign writing.

Plasterer – works with plaster, cement mixes, plasterboard and expanded metal, to finish walls, ceilings and floors; also makes and fixes plaster decorations.

Plumber – works with metals, plastics and ceramics; installs tanks, baths, toilets, sinks, basins, rainwater goods, boilers, radiators, and gas appliances; also cuts and fixes sheet-metal roof covering and flashing and sometimes glazing; also maintains existing works.

Roof slater and tiler – works with felt, timber, metals, mortar and a wide variety of slates and tiles; covers new or existing pitched roofs with slates or tiles; also maintains existing works.

Shopfitter – works with timber, metal, glass and plastics, etc.; makes and installs shop fronts and interiors, also for banks, hotels, offices and restaurants.

Stonemason – works with stone and mortar; 'bankers' cut and smooth stone while 'fixers' erect prepared stones.

Woodworking machinist – operates a wide range of woodworking machines; prepares timber for the production of timber-building components.

Building operatives – Two main types are employed on-site:

The *general building operative* uses various items of plant, e.g. hand tools, power tools, compressors and concreting equipment, etc.; mixes concrete, mortar and plaster; lays drainage, kerb stones and concrete, etc.; off-loads materials and transports around site; also generally assists the work of craft operatives.

The *specialist building operative* carries out specialist building operations, e.g. ceiling fixer, dry liner, glazier, mastic asphalter, built-up felt roofer, plant mechanic, roof sheeter and cladder, scaffolder, wall and floor tiler, etc.

TRY AND ANSWER THESE

Questions for you

1. Name **THREE** of the main areas of work which make up the building industry.

2. State the difference between private and public sector building work.

3. Name **THREE** examples of building work.

4. Name **THREE** examples of civil engineering work.

5. State the difference between maintenance, refurbishment and restoration.

6. State the main purpose of the construction industry.

7. State the classification of a contractor with 100 employees.

The building team

The construction of a building is a complex process, which requires a team of professionals working together to produce the desired results. This team of professionals, which is collectively known as the building team, is a combination of the following parties:

Client
Architect
Quantity surveyor
Specialist engineers
Clerk of works
Local authority
Health and safety inspector
Building contractors
Sub-contractors
Suppliers

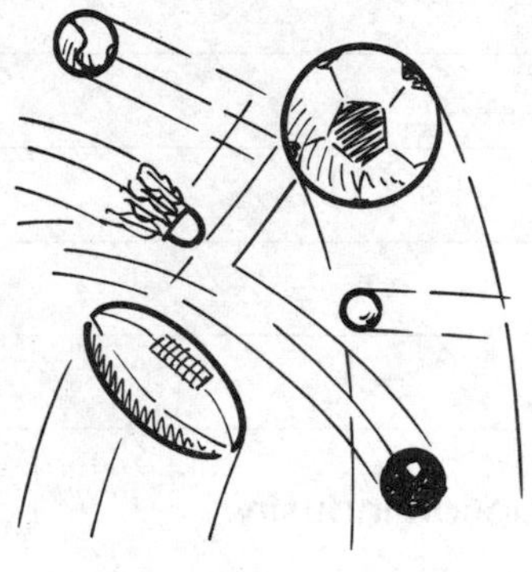

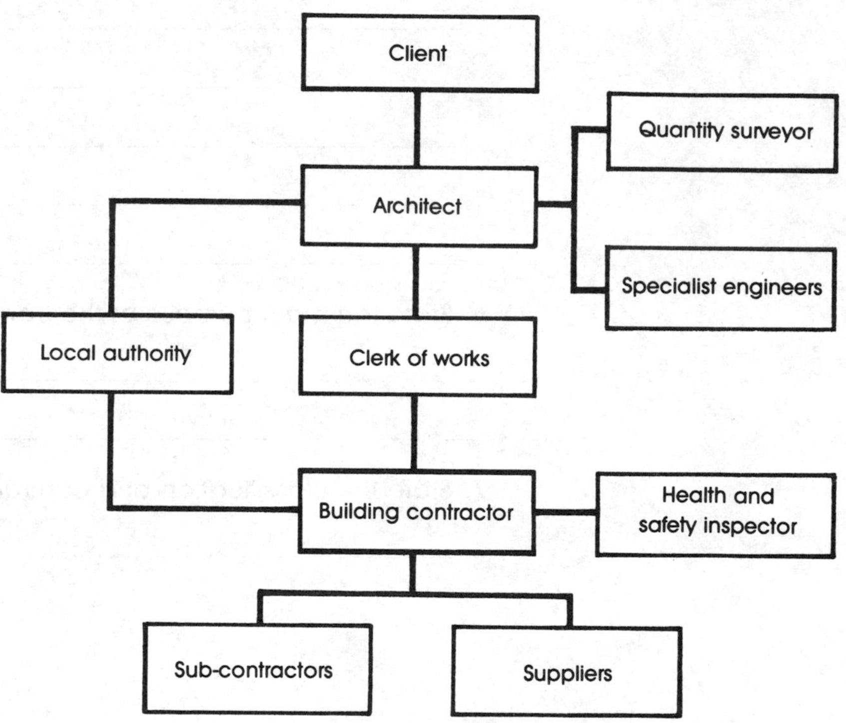

Client

This is the person or persons who have an actual need for building work, e.g. the construction of a new house, office block, factory or extensions, repairs and alterations to existing buildings. The client is the most important member of the building team, without them the work would simply not exist. He/she is responsible for the overall financing of the work and in effect employs either directly or indirectly the entire team. The type of client can vary from a single person to a very large organisation, for example:

Private individual	Local authority
Association	Nationalised industry
Partnership	Statutory undertaking
Public company	Government department.

Architect

The architect is the client's agent and is considered to be the leader of the building team. The role of an architect is to interpret the client's requirements, translate them into a building form and generally supervise all aspects of the work until it is completed. All architects must be registered with the Architects' Registration Council, the majority of them also being members of the Royal Institute of British Architects, using the designatory letters RIBA.

Quantity surveyor

In effect, the quantity surveyor or QS as they are often termed is the client's building economic consultant or accountant. This specialist surveyor advises during the design stage as to how the building may be constructed within the client's budget, and measures the quantity of labour and materials necessary to complete the building work from drawings and other information prepared and supplied by the architect. These quantities are incorporated into a document known as the **bill of quantities** which is used by the building contractors when pricing the building work. During the contract, the quantity surveyor will measure and prepare valuations of the work carried out to date to enable interim payments to be made to the building contractor. At the end of the building contract they will prepare the final account for presentation to the client. In addition, the quantity surveyor will advise the architect on the cost of additional works or variations.

Specialist engineers

These are engaged as part of the design team to assist the architect in the design of the building within their specialist fields, e.g. civil engineer, structural engineer, service engineer.

They will prepare drawings and calculations to enable specialist contractors to quote for these areas of work. In addition, during the contract the specialist engineers will make regular inspections to ensure the installation is carried out in accordance with the design.

Clerk of works

The clerk of works is appointed by the architect/client to act as their on-site representative. On large contracts they will be resident on-site whilst on smaller ones they will only visit periodically. The clerk of works or COW is an 'inspector of works' and as such will ensure that the contractor carries out the work in accordance with the drawings and other contract documents. This includes inspecting both the standard of workmanship and the quality of materials. The COW will make regular reports back to the architect, keep a diary in case of disputes, make a daily record of the weather, and/or personnel employed on-site and any stoppage. They also agree general matters directly with the building contractor although these must be confirmed by the architect to be valid.

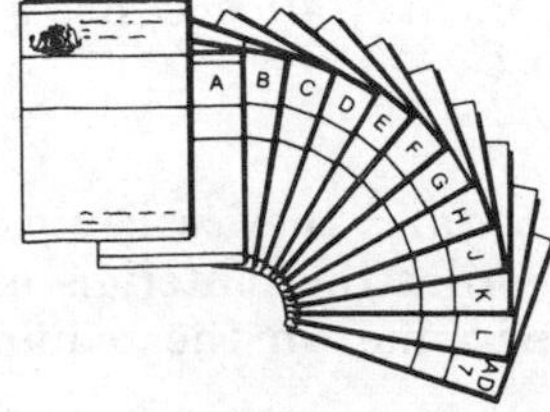

The local authority

The local authority normally has the responsibility of ensuring that proposed building works conform to the requirements of relevant planning and building legislation. For this purpose, they employ planning officers and building control officers to approve and inspect building work. In some areas they are called building inspectors or district surveyors (DS).

Health and safety inspector

The health and safety inspector (also known as the factory inspector) is employed by the Health and Safety Executive. It is the inspector's duty to ensure that the government legislation concerning health and safety is fully implemented by the building contractor.

Building contractor

The building contractor enters into a contract with the client to carry out, in accordance with the contract documents, certain building works. Each contractor will develop their own method and procedures for tendering and carrying out building work which in turn, together with the size of the contract, will determine the personnel required.

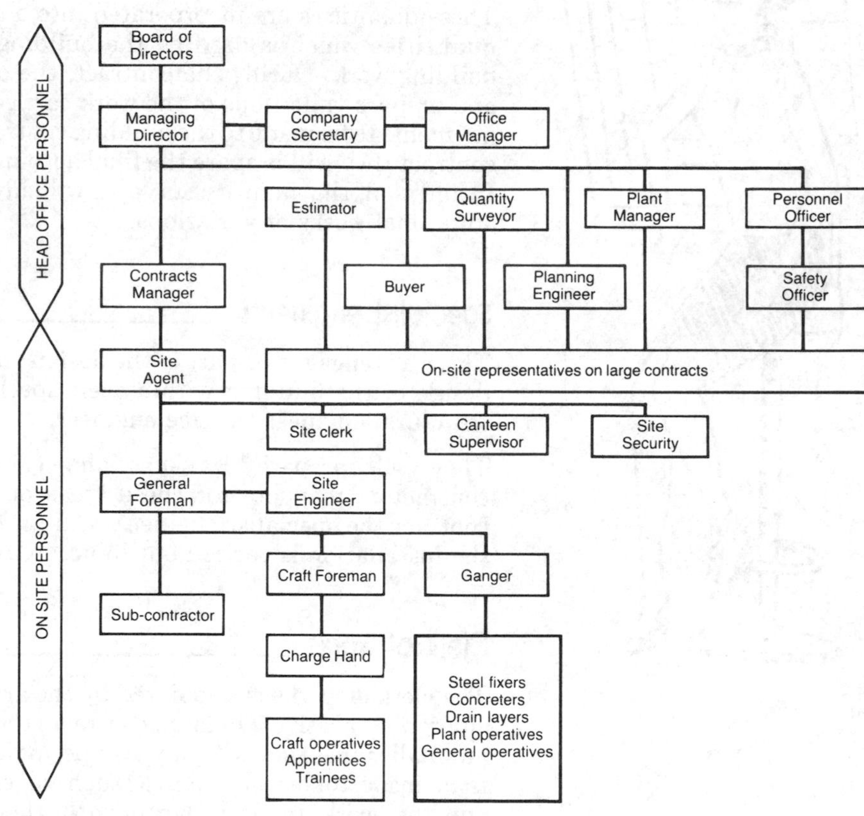

A typical contractor's organisation structure

Estimator – arrives at an overall cost for carrying out a building contract. In order to arrive at the overall cost they will break down each item contained in the bill of quantities into its constituent parts (labour, materials and plant) and apply a rate to each, representing the amount it will cost the contractor to complete the item. Added to the total cost of all items will be a percentage for overheads (head/site office costs, site management/administration salaries) and profit.

Buyer – responsible for the purchase of materials; they will obtain quotations, negotiate the best possible terms, order the materials and ensure that they arrive on-site at the required time, in the required quantity and quality.

Building contractor's quantity surveyor – the building contractor's building economist; they will measure and evaluate the building work carried out each month including the work of any subcontractors. An interim valuation is prepared by them on the basis of these measurements and passed on to the client for payment. They are also responsible for preparing interim costings to see whether or not the contract is within budget; finally they will prepare and agree the final accounts on completion of the contract.

Planning engineer – responsible for the pre-contract planning of the building project. It is their role to plan the work in such a way as to ensure the most efficient/economical use of labour, materials, plant and equipment. Within their specialist field of work planning engineers are often supported by a work study engineer (to examine various building operations to increase productivity) and a bonus surveyor (to operate an incentive scheme which is also aimed at increasing productivity by awarding operatives additional money for work completed over a basic target).

Plant manager – responsible for all items of mechanical plant (machines and power tools) used by the building contractor. At the request of the contracts manager/site agent they will supply from stock, purchase or hire, the most suitable plant item to carry out a specific task. The plant manager is also responsible for the maintenance of plant items and the training of operatives who use them.

Safety officer – responsible to senior management for all aspects of health and safety. They advise on all health and safety matters, carry out safety inspections, keep safety records, investigate accidents and arrange staff safety training.

Note: Each of the head-office personnel previously mentioned is the leader of a specialist service section and depending on the size of the firm will employ one or more technicians for assistance. On very large contracts they may also have a representative resident on-site.

Contracts manager – the supervisor/coordinator of the site's management team, on a number of contracts. The contracts manager has an overall responsibility for planning, management and building operations. They will liaise between the head office staff and the site agents on the contracts for which they are responsible.

Site agent – also known as the site manager or project manager, the site agent is the building contractor's resident on-site representative and leader of the site work force. They are directly responsible to the contracts manager for the day-to-day planning, management and building operations.

General foreman – works under the site agent and is responsible for co-ordinating the work of the craft foreman, ganger and subcontractors. They will also advise the site agent on constructional problems, liaise with the clerk of works and may also be responsible for the day-to-day employing and dismissing of operatives. On smaller contracts which may not require a site agent the general foreman will have total responsibility for the site.

Site engineer – sometimes called the surveyor, works alongside the general foreman. They are responsible for ensuring that the building is the correct size and in the right place. They will set out and check the line, level and vertical (plumb) of the building during its construction.

Craft foreman – works under the general foreman to organise and supervise the work of a specific craft, e.g. foreman bricklayer and foreman carpenter.

Ganger – like the craft foreman, the ganger also works under the general foreman but is responsible for the organisation and supervision of the general building operatives.

Chargehand – on large contracts employing a large number of craft operatives in each craft (normally bricklayers and carpenters), chargehands are often appointed to assist the craft foreman and supervise a subsection of the work. For example, a foreman carpenter may have chargehands to supervise the carcassing team (floor joists and roofs); the first fixing team (flooring, frames and studwork); the second fixing team (doors, skirting, architraves and joinery fitments). Chargehands are often known as working foremen because, in addition to supervising their small team, they also carry out the skilled physical work of their craft.

Operative – the person who carries out the actual physical building work. Operatives can be divided into two main groups:

Craft operatives are the skilled craftsmen who perform specialist tasks with a range of materials, e.g. bricklayer, carpenter, electrician, painter, plasterer and plumber.

Building operatives are further subdivided into general building operatives, who mix concrete, lay drains, off-load material and assist craft operatives; and specialist building operatives, e.g. ceiling fixer, glazier, plant mechanic and scaffolder.

Site clerk – responsible for all site administrative duties and the control of materials on-site. They will record the arrival and departure of all site personnel, prepare wage sheets for head office, record the delivery and transfer of plant items, record and check delivery of materials and note their ultimate distribution (assisted by a storekeeper).

The sub-contractor

The building contractor may call upon a specialist firm to carry out a specific part of the building work; for this they will enter into a sub-contract, hence the term sub-contractor. Building contractors generally sub-contract work such as structural steelwork, formwork, mechanical services, electrical installations, plastering, tiling and often painting. However, at certain times they may also sub-contract the major crafts of bricklaying and carpentry. Sub-contractors may be labour-only (where they contract to fit the building contractor's material), or they may contract to supply and fix their own material. Architects can name or nominate a specific sub-contractor in the contract documents and this sub-contractor must be used. They are then known as nominated sub-contractors.

The suppliers

Building materials, equipment and plant are supplied by a wide range of merchants, manufacturers and hirers. The building contractor will negotiate with these to supply their goods in the required quantity and quality, at the agreed price, and finally in accordance with the building contractor's delivery requirements. Architects may nominate specific suppliers who must be used and are therefore termed nominated suppliers.

TRY AND ANSWER THESE

Questions for you

8. Name and describe the role of **FOUR** members of the building team.

9. List the persons who would be employed in the design of a building.

10. Name the person who is responsible for checking the standard of work on behalf of the client on site.

11. Name the person who is responsible for protection against injury on site.

12. Name **THREE** craft operatives and give an example of the work **EACH** carries out.

13. Explain the term 'general operative'.

14. Explain the term 'sub-contractor'.

15. A specification for building works is normally prepared for a client by the:
(a) building control officer
(b) clerk of works
(c) estimator
(d) quantity surveyor

a [ ]	b [ ]	c [ ]	d [ ]

16. Name the job title of the person who controls a number of building contracts.

17. List ten occupations of people employed by a building contractor.

Principles of construction

Types of building

A structure is defined as an organised combination of connected parts (elements) which are constructed to perform a required function, e.g. a bridge. A building takes this idea a step further and is used to define structures that enclose space using an external envelope.

The external envelope is simply the walls or covering material which provide the desired internal conditions for the building's occupants with regard to: security, safety, privacy, warmth, light and ventilation, etc.

Buildings are classified into three main categories according to their height.

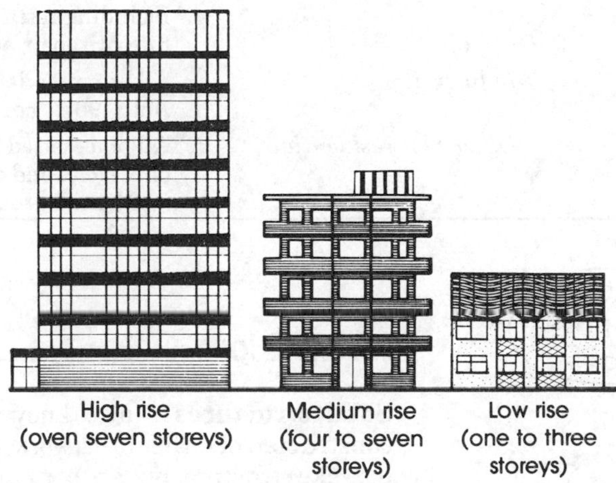

These categories are further subdivided into a wide variety of basic shapes, styles and groupings, for example:

Detached – a building that is unconnected with adjacent ones.

Semi-detached – a building which is joined to one adjacent building but is detached from any other. It will share one dividing or party wall.

Terraced – a row of three or more adjoining buildings, the inner ones of which will share two party walls.

Another method of categorising buildings which is used in statutory regulations groups buildings according to their purpose.

Detached

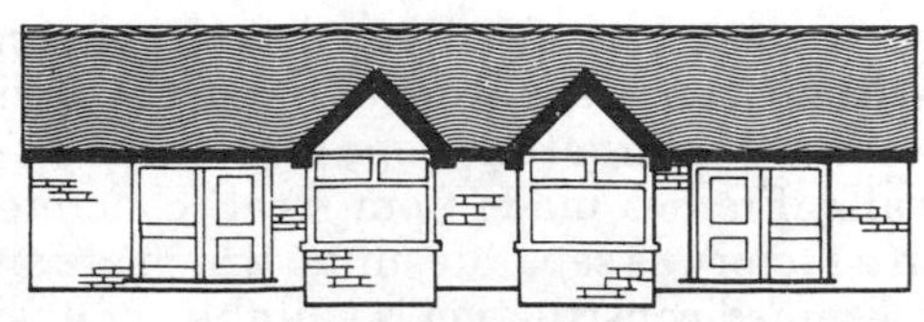
Semi-detached

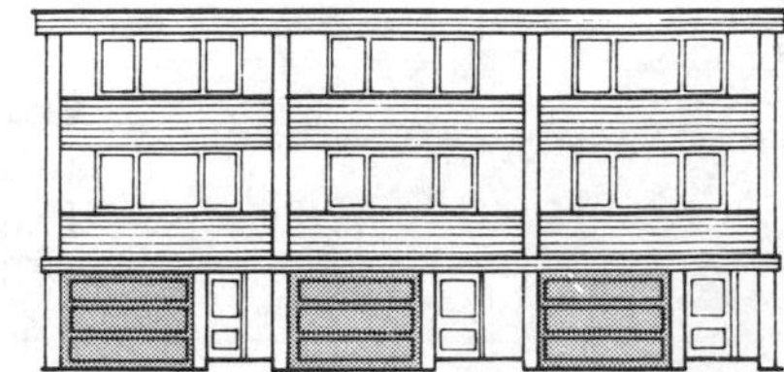
Terraced

Purpose groups

Main category	*Purpose group*	*Intended use*
Residential	*Dwelling house* (not a flat or maisonette)	Private dwelling house
	Flat (including a maisonette)	Self-contained dwelling not being a house
	Institutional	Hospitals, schools and homes used as living accommodation for persons suffering from disabilities owing to illness, old age, physical or mental disorders and those under five years old, where these persons sleep on the premises
	Other residential	Residential accommodation not included in previous groups, e.g. hotels, boarding houses, and hostels, etc.
Non-residential	*Assembly*	Public building or assembly building where people meet for social, recreational, or business activities (not office, shop or industrial)
	Office	All premises used for administration procedures, e.g. clerical, drawing, publishing and banking, etc.
	Shop	All premises used for the retail sale of goods or services, including restaurants, public houses, cafes, hairdressers and hire or repair outlets
	Industrial	All premises defined as a factory in Section 175 of the Factories Act (1961), not including slaughter houses etc.
	Other non-residential	All places used for the deposit or storage of goods, the parking of vehicles and other premises not covered in the previous non-residential groups

Structural form

Solid structures – also known as mass wall construction. Walls are constructed of either brickwork, blockwork or concrete. They form a stable box-like structure, but are normally limited to low-rise, short-span buildings.

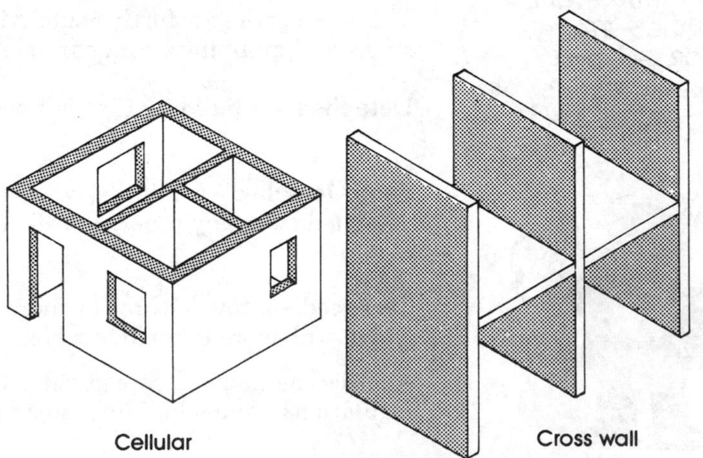

Framed structures – also termed skeleton construction, this consists of an inter-connected framework of members having a supporting function. The protecting external envelope is provided by either external cladding or infill walls. Frames made from steel, concrete or timber are often pre-made in a factory as separate units, which are simply and speedily erected on site. Framed construction is suitable for a wide range of buildings and civil engineering structures from low to high rise.

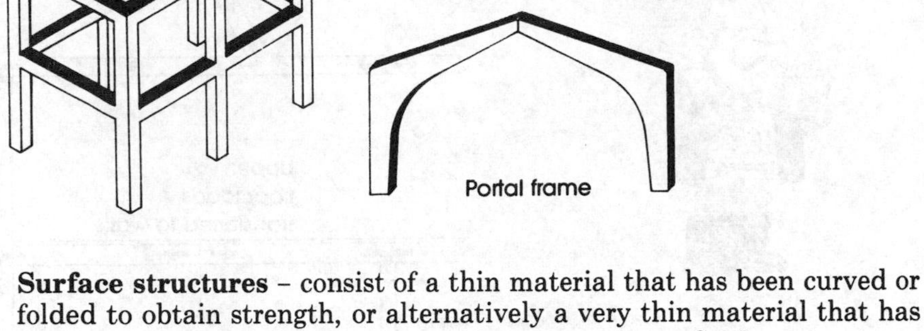

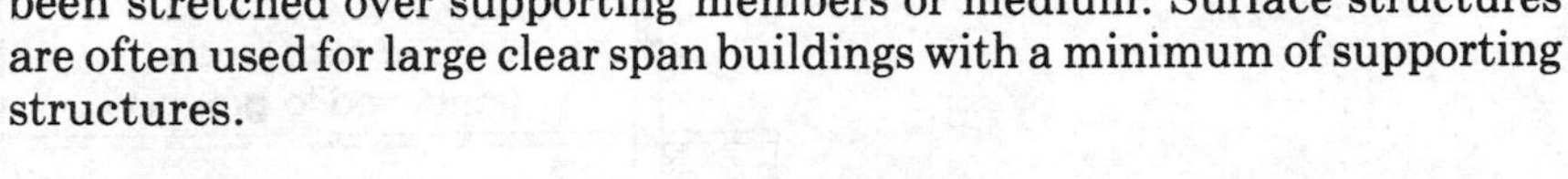

Surface structures - consist of a thin material that has been curved or folded to obtain strength, or alternatively a very thin material that has been stretched over supporting members or medium. Surface structures are often used for large clear span buildings with a minimum of supporting structures.

Shell roof

Air supported

Surface structures

Structural parts

All structures consist of two main parts: that below ground and that above ground.

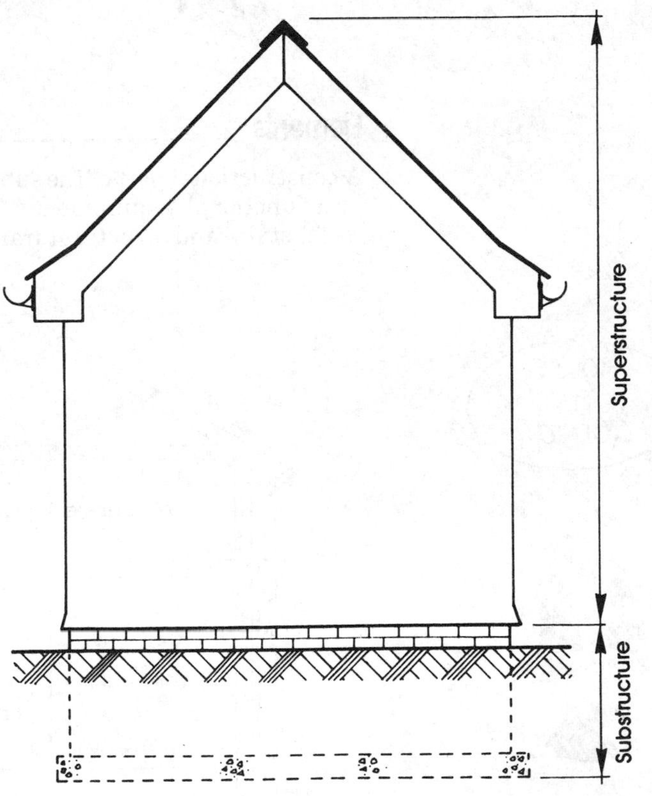

Substructure - all of the structure below ground and that up to and including the ground floor slab and damp-proof course. Its purpose is to receive the loads from the main building superstructure and transfer them safely down to a suitable load-bearing layer of ground.

Superstructure - all of the structure above the substructure both internally and externally. Its purpose is to enclose and divide space, and transfer loads safely on to the substructure.

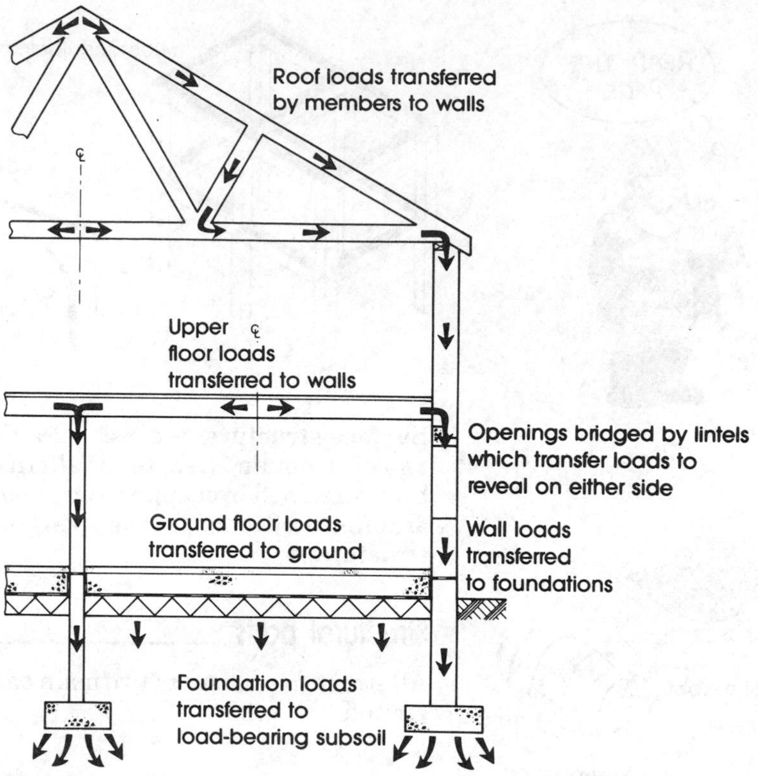

Elements

A constructional part of the sub- or superstructure of a building having its own functional requirements. These include foundations, walls, floors, roofs, stairs and structural framework.

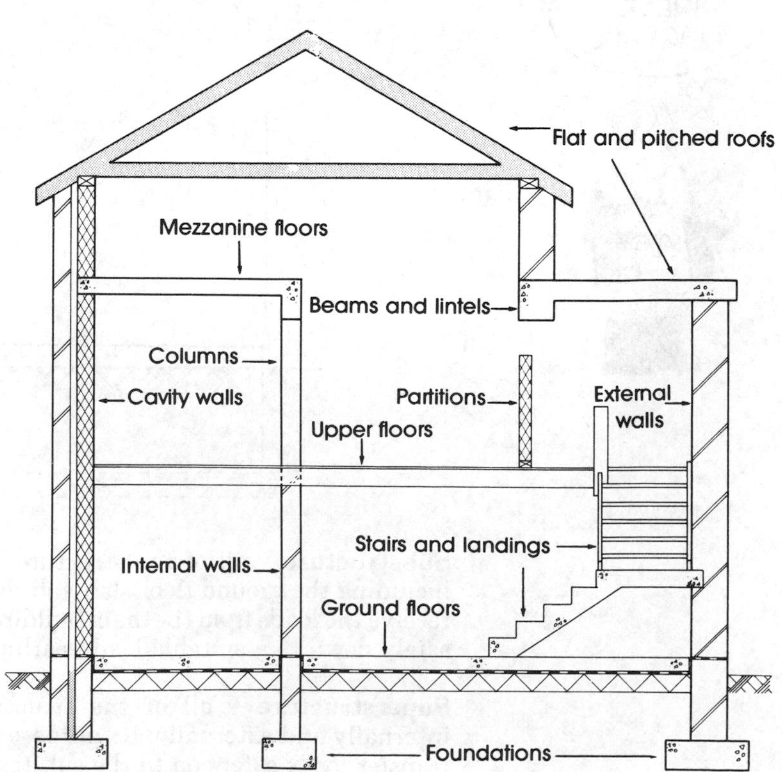

READ THIS PAGE
LOAD

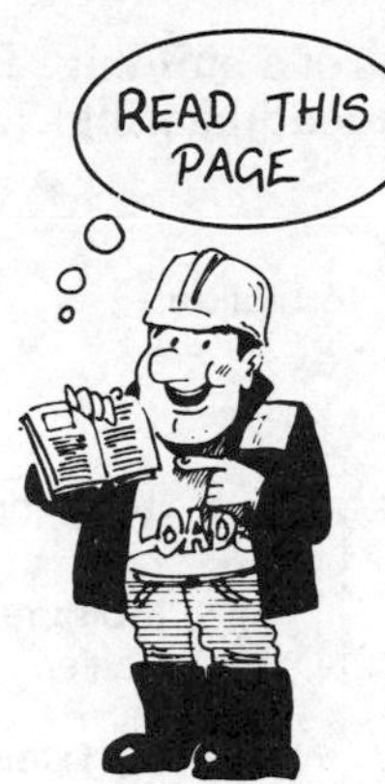

Primary elements – the main supporting, enclosing or protection elements of a building. Also those that divide space and provide floor-to-floor access.

Foundations are a primary element that transfer the loads of a structure safely on to the ground.

Brick and block cavity wall
DPC
Oversite concrete
DPM
Hardcore
Fine concrete cavity fill (below ground level)
Strip
Deep strip (trench fill)

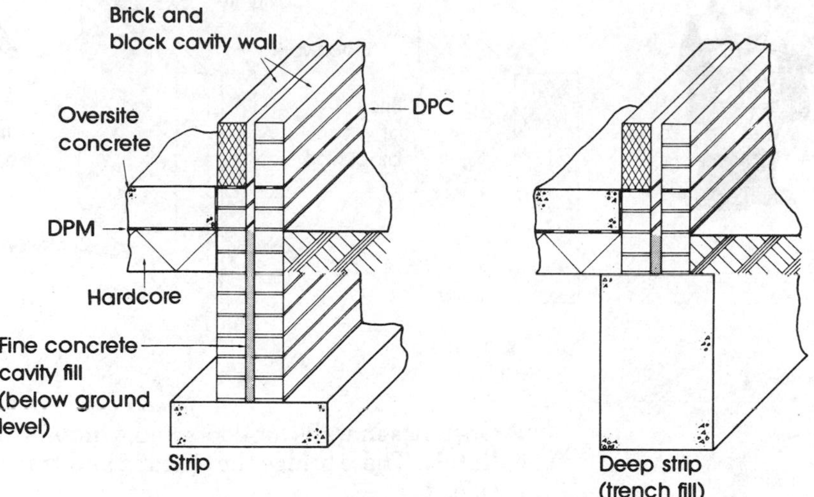

Strip foundations

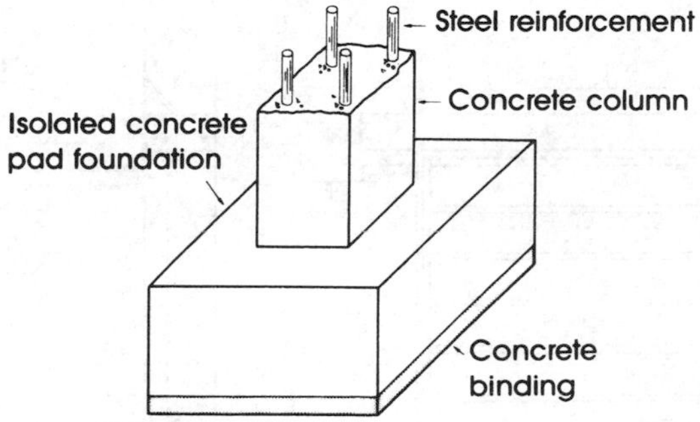

Steel reinforcement
Concrete column
Isolated concrete pad foundation
Concrete binding

Pad foundation

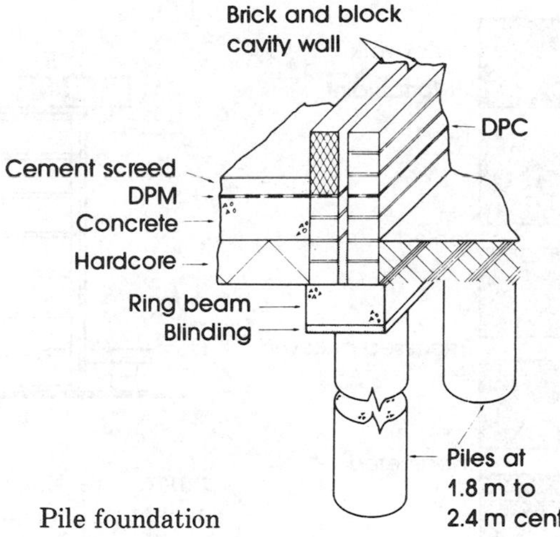

Brick and block cavity wall
DPC
Cement screed
DPM
Concrete
Hardcore
Ring beam
Blinding
Piles at 1.8 m to 2.4 m centres

Pile foundation

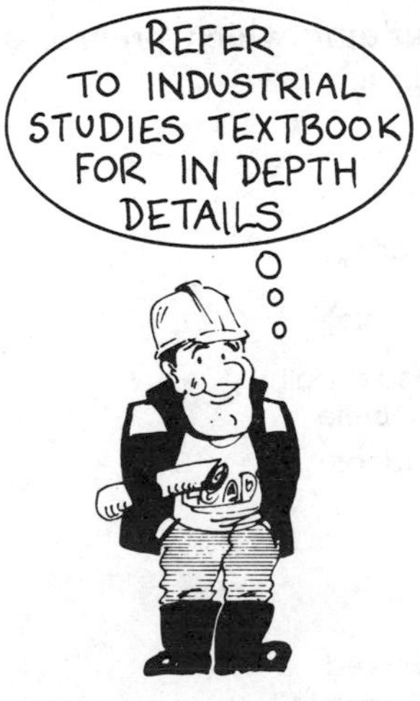

REFER TO INDUSTRIAL STUDIES TEXTBOOK FOR IN DEPTH DETAILS

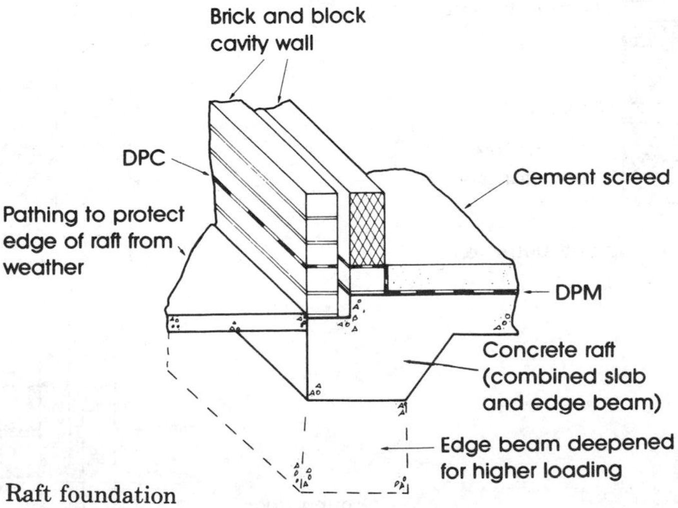

Brick and block cavity wall
DPC
Cement screed
Pathing to protect edge of raft from weather
DPM
Concrete raft (combined slab and edge beam)
Edge beam deepened for higher loading

Raft foundation

Walls are the vertical enclosing and dividing elements of a building. They may be load-bearing or simply to divide space (non-load-bearing).

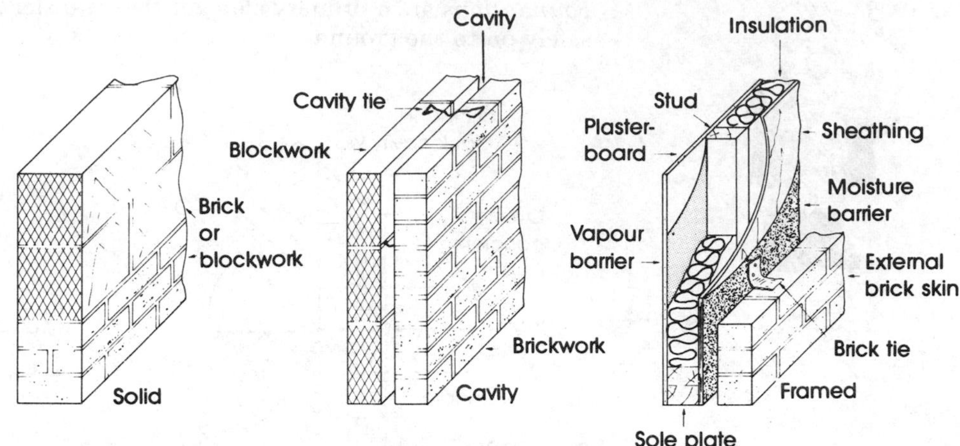

Openings in walls for doors and windows are spanned by steel or concrete **lintels**. These bridge the opening and transfer loads to the reveal on either side.

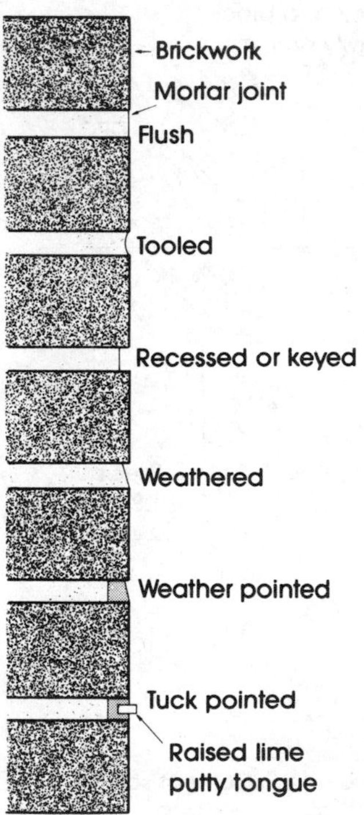

Wall jointing and pointing

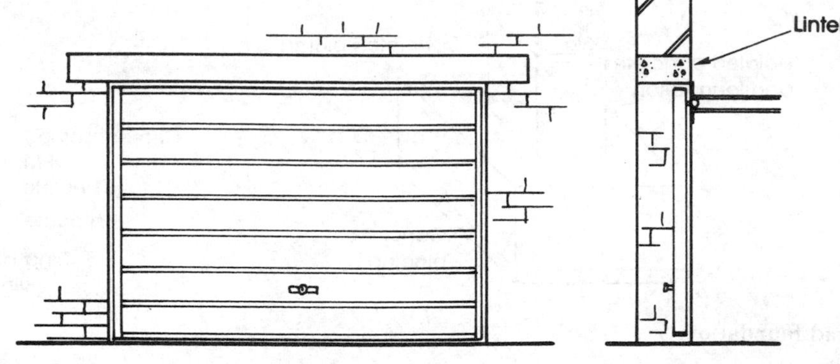

Floors are the ground or upper levels in a building which provide an acceptable surface for walking, living and working.

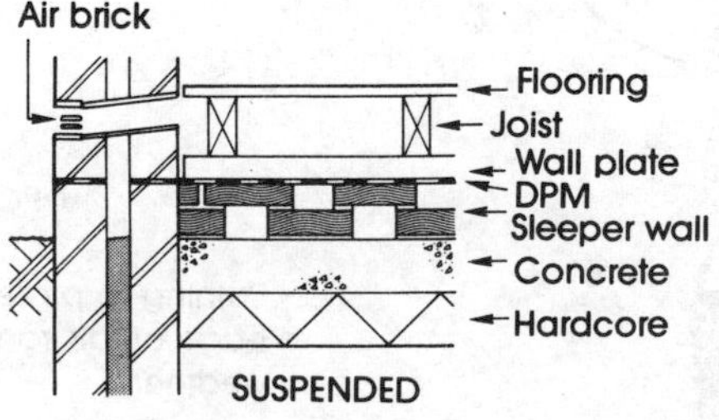

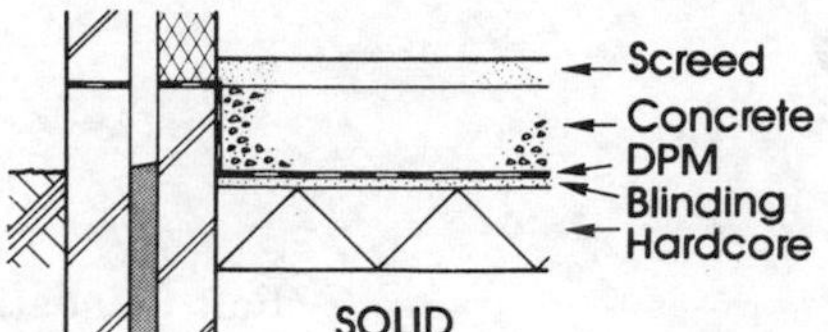

Ground floors

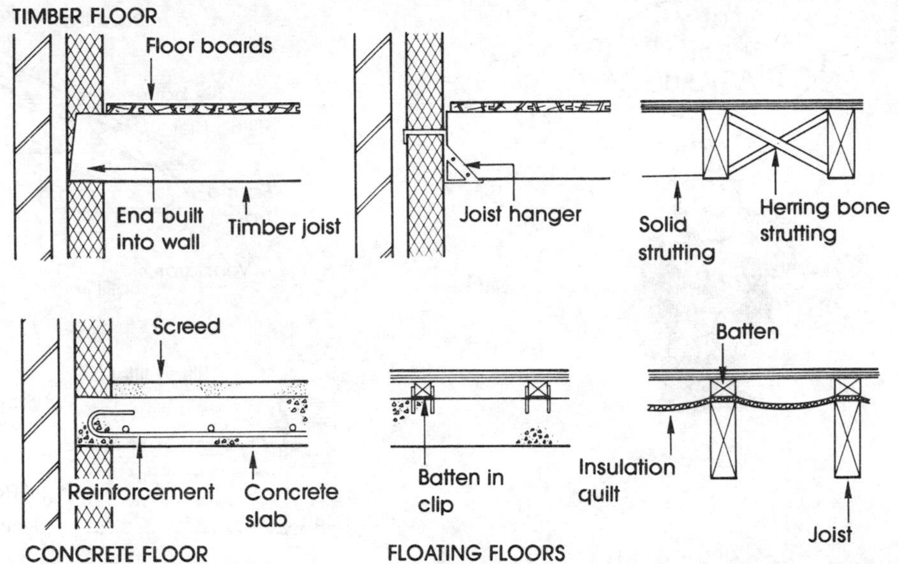

Upper floors

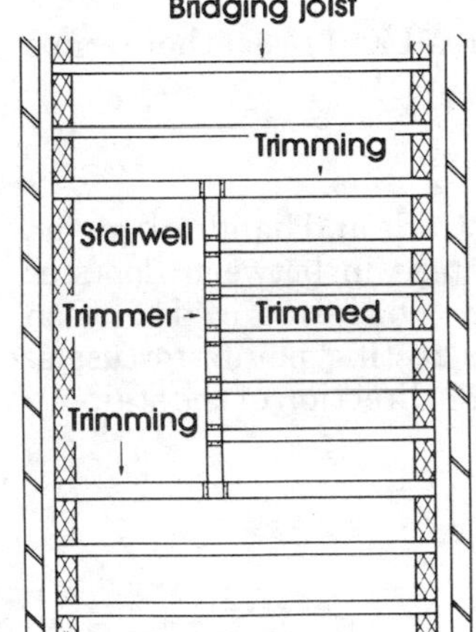

Where openings for stairs etc. occur in timber upper floors, the joists have to be framed or trimmed

Roofs are the uppermost part of a building that span the walls to provide weathering and insulation. Mainly flat or pitched but variously named according to shape.

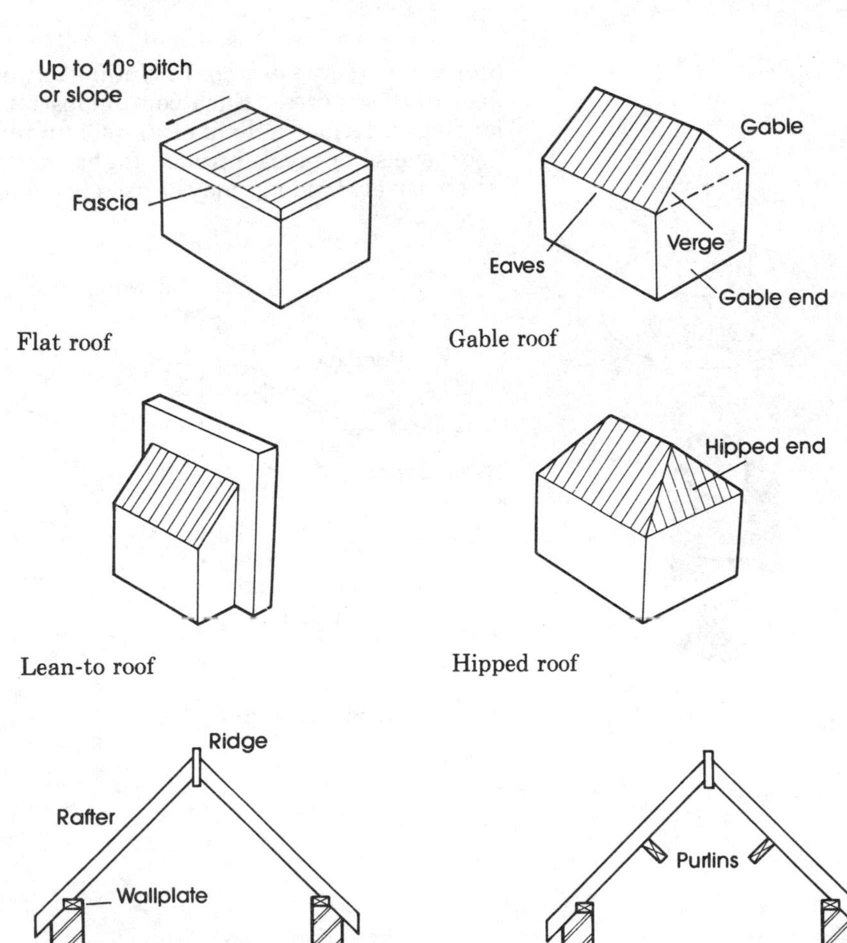

Flat roof

Gable roof

Lean-to roof

Hipped roof

Single roof

Double roof

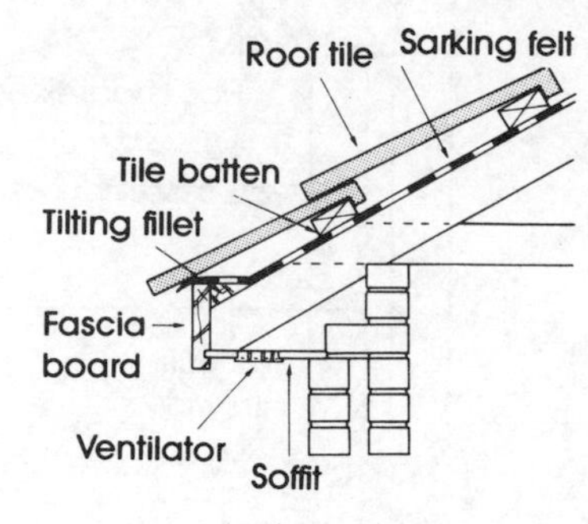

Eaves

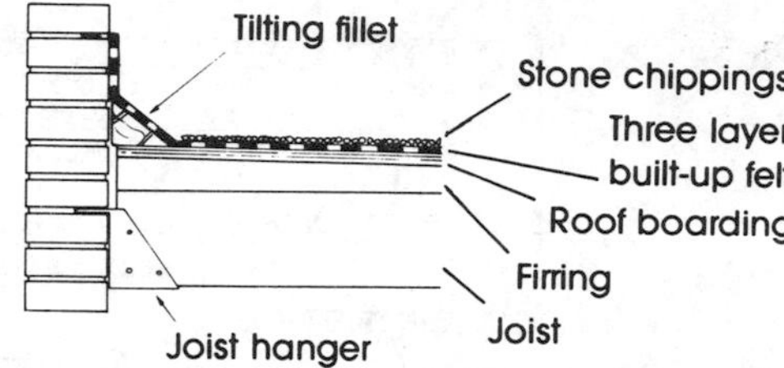

Flat roof at abutment

Stairs are the series of steps (combination of tread and riser) that form a stairway.

Stairway – a series of steps (including any balustrade and handrail) giving floor-to-floor access. Each continuous set of steps in between floors or landings is termed a flight of stairs. Landings may be introduced between floor levels, to break up long flights and give resting points for users. Alternatively landings may be used to change the direction of the stair.

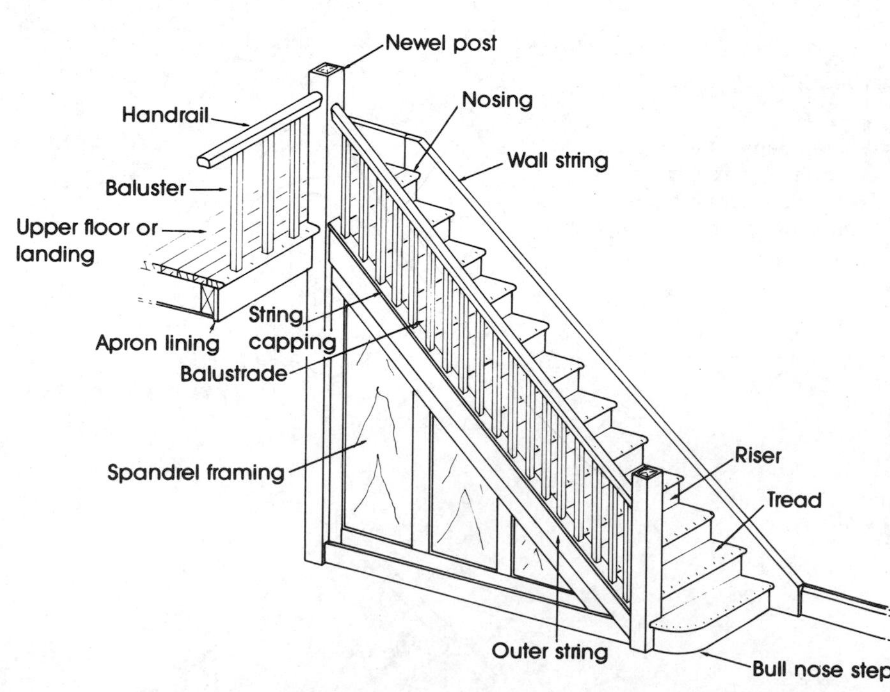

Secondary elements – the non-essential elements of a structure, having mainly a completion role around openings in primary elements.

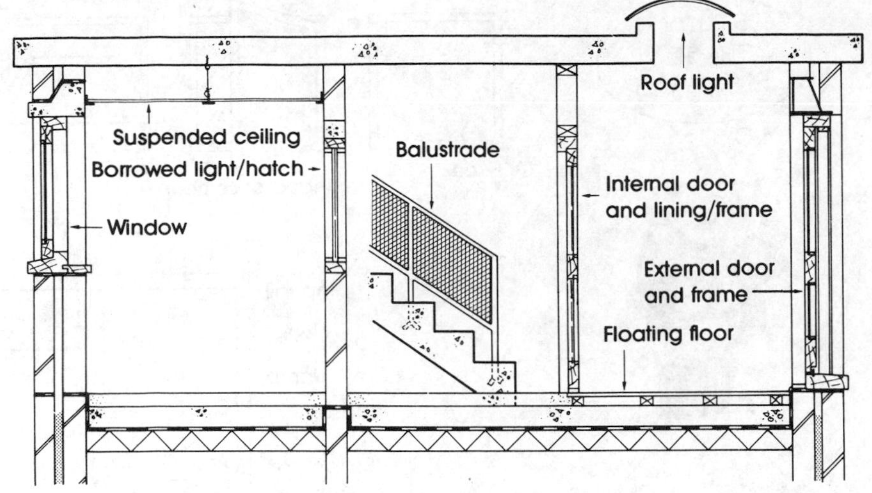

Secondary elements

Doors are moveable barriers used to cover an opening in a structure. Their main function is to allow access in a building and passage between its interior spaces. Other functional requirements include weather protection, fire resistance, sound and thermal insulation, security, privacy, ease of operation and durability. They may be classified by their method of construction and method of operation.

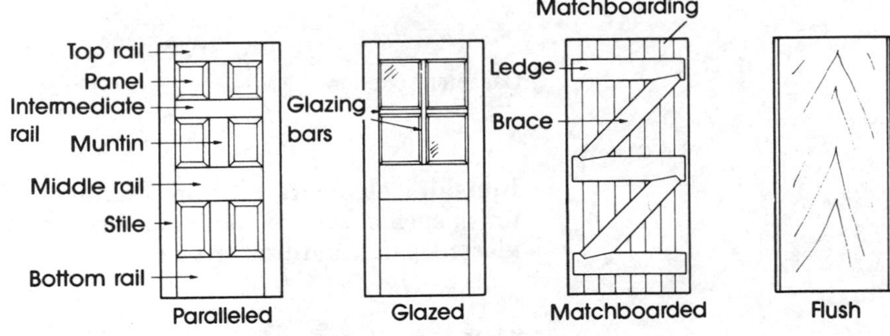

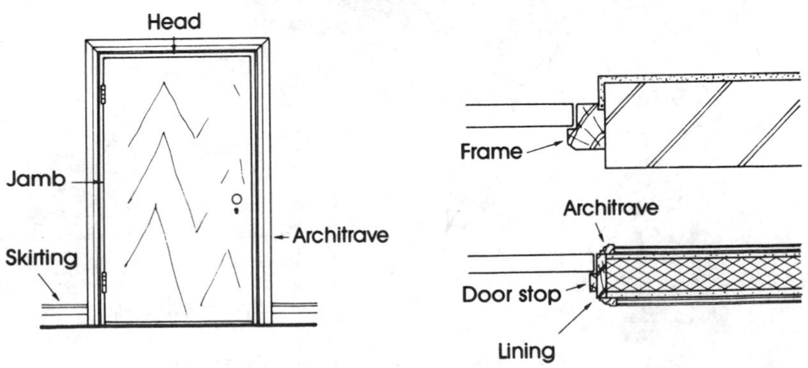

The surround to the wall opening on which doors are hung may be either a *frame* or *lining*.

Windows are glazed openings in a wall used to allow daylight and air in and give occupants an outside view.

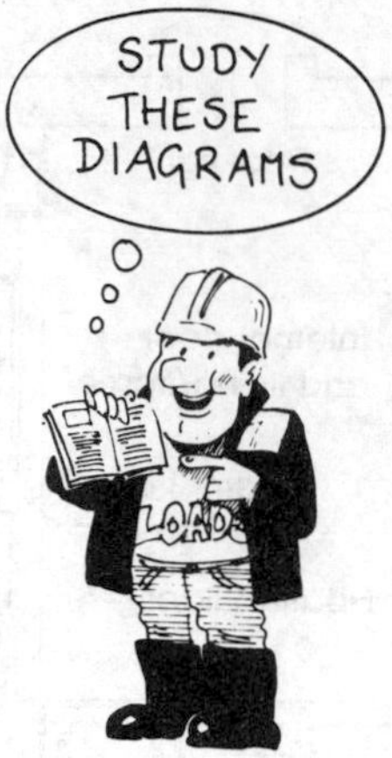

STUDY THESE DIAGRAMS

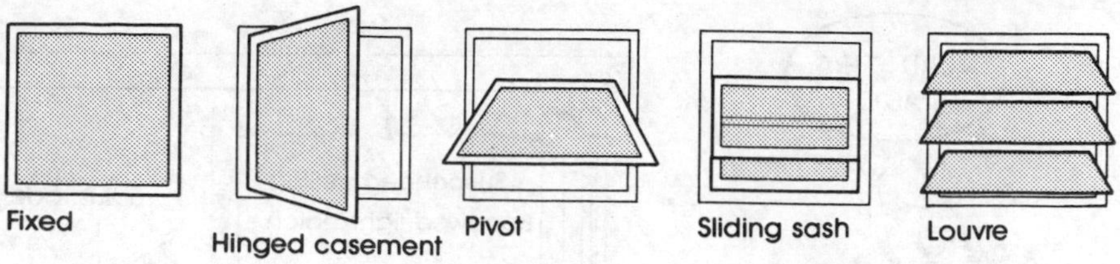

Fixed
Hinged casement
Pivot
Sliding sash
Louvre

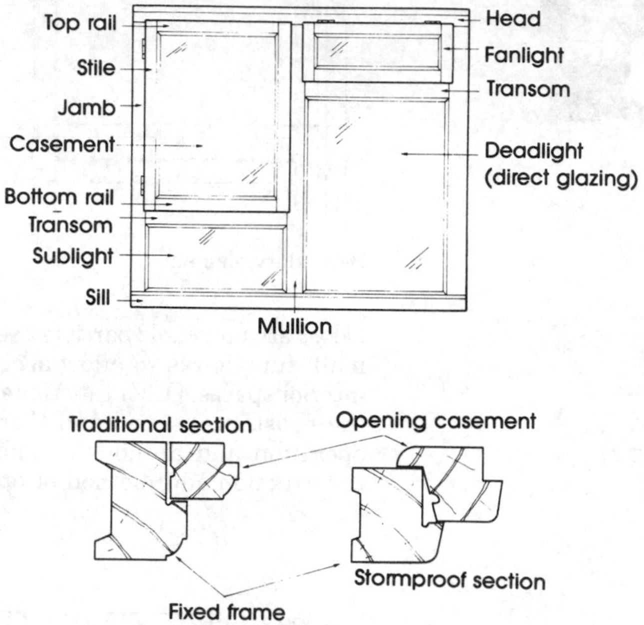

Top rail
Stile
Jamb
Casement
Bottom rail
Transom
Sublight
Sill
Mullion
Head
Fanlight
Transom
Deadlight
(direct glazing)
Traditional section
Opening casement
Stormproof section
Fixed frame

Casement window

Finishing elements – the final surface of an element that may be a self-finish such as concrete and face brickwork, or an applied finish such as plaster, paint and timber trim.

HOW'S IT GOING?

Roof tiles
or slates
Dry lining
Paint system
Architrave
Picture rail
Flashing
Felt and
chippings
Wallpaper
Plinth block
Skirting
Tile
hanging
Plasterboard ceiling
Cornice
Plaster
Timber
cladding
Dado rail
Panelling
Cement
screed
Tiles
Wood block
Cement
rendering

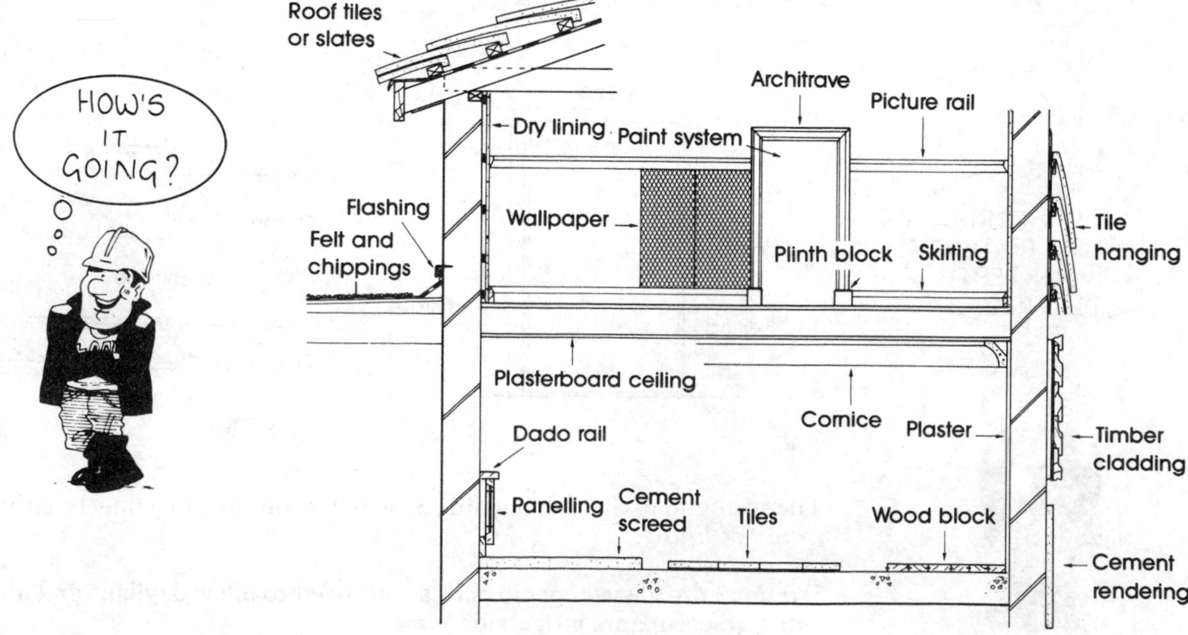

Components – the various parts or materials that are combined to form the elements of a building.

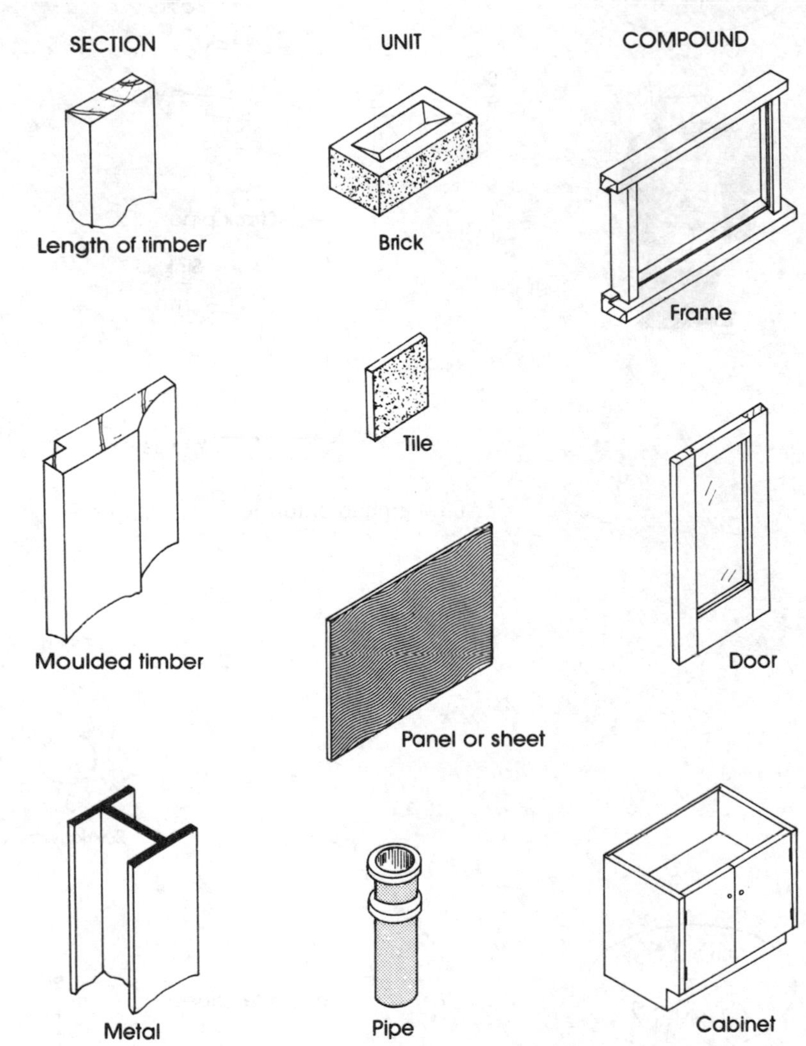

Services – the electrical, plumbing, mechanical and specialist installations in a building, normally piped, wired or ducted into or within a building.

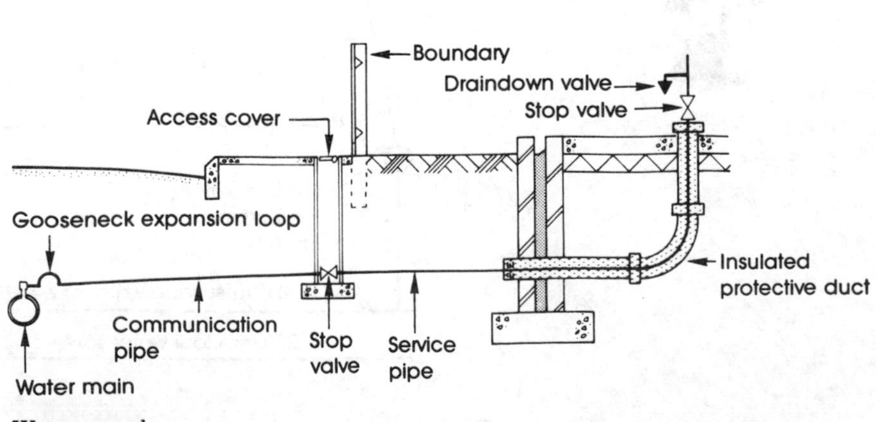

Water supply

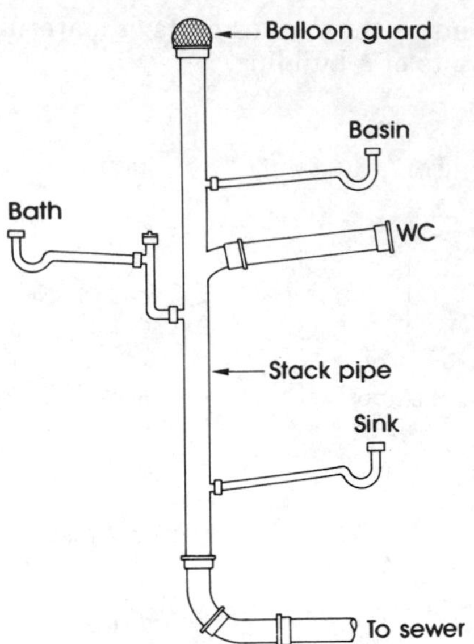

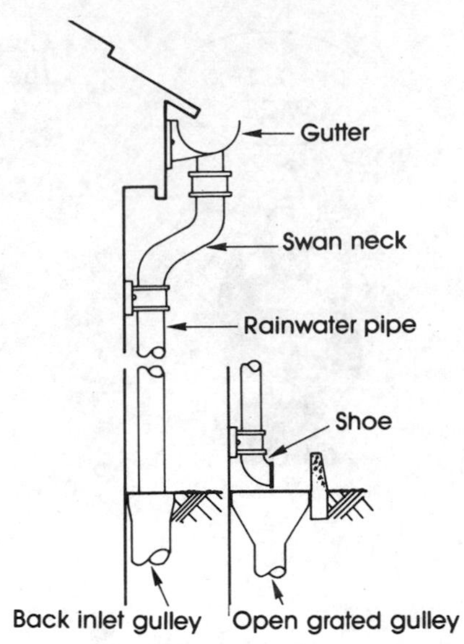

Above ground drainage

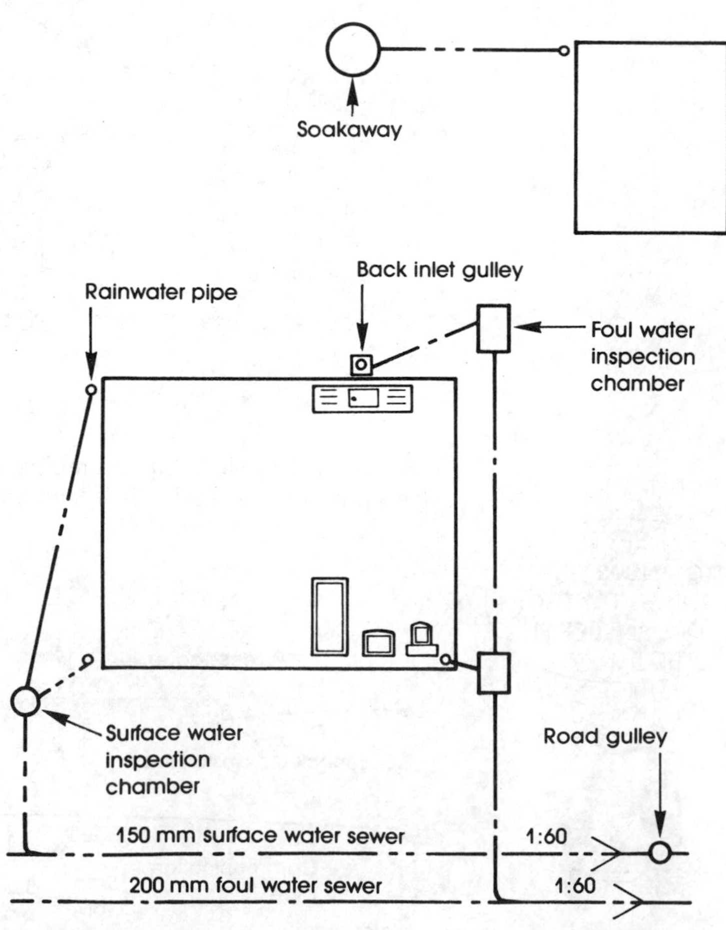

Below ground drainage

Site works

Excavation – the process of removing earth to form a hole in the ground can be dug manually using a shovel or mechanically using a digger excavator.

Oversite excavation is the removal of topsoil and vegetable matter from a site prior to the commencement of building work. Excavation depth is typically between 150 and 300 mm.

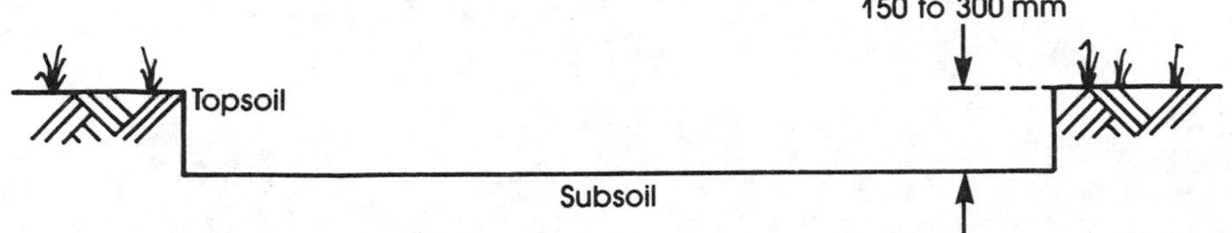

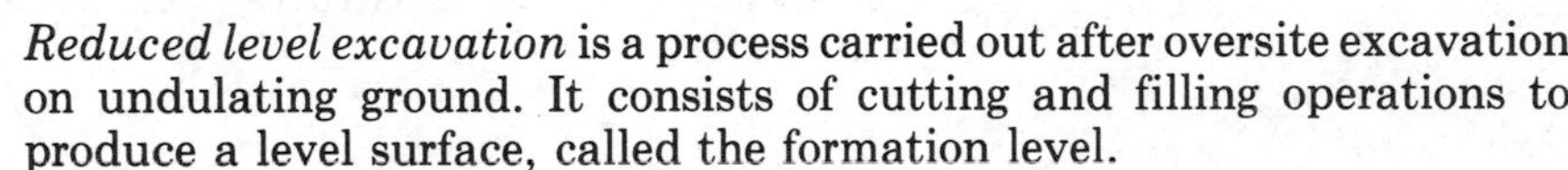

Reduced level excavation is a process carried out after oversite excavation on undulating ground. It consists of cutting and filling operations to produce a level surface, called the formation level.

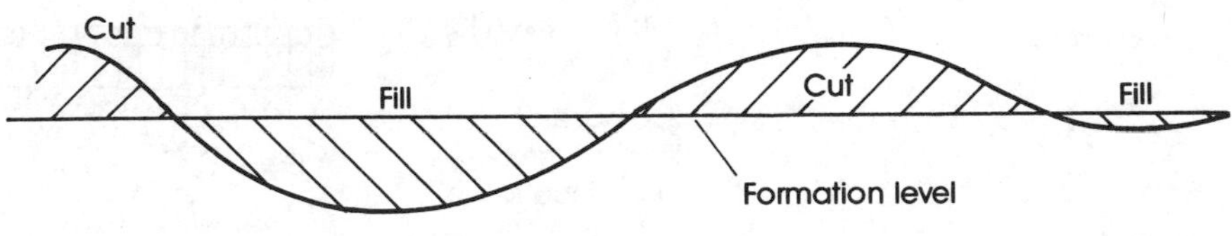

Trench excavations are long narrow holes in the ground, to accommodate strip foundations or underground services. Deep trenches may be battered or timbered to prevent the sides from caving in.

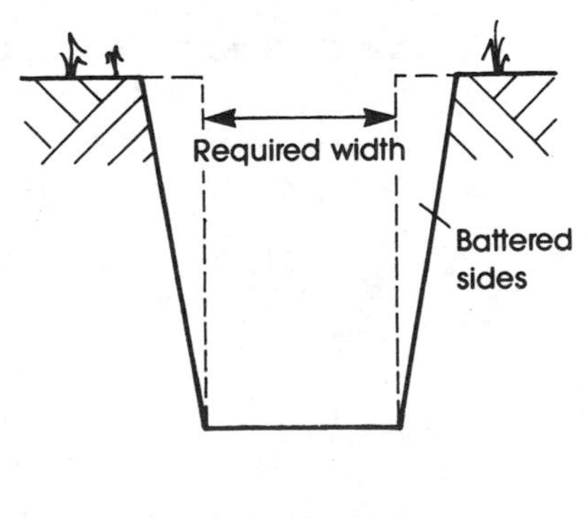

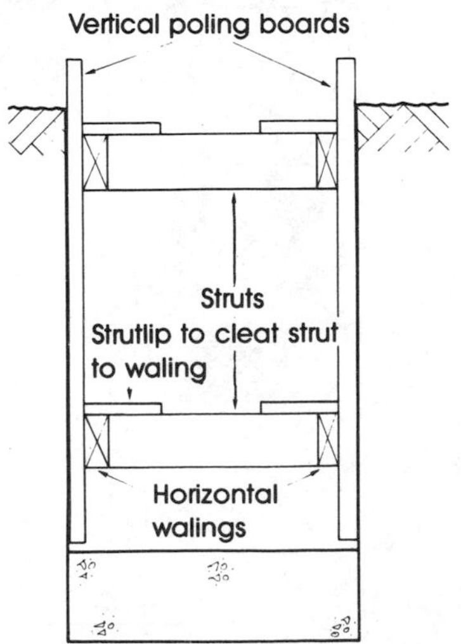

Timbering to sides of trench

Pit excavations are deep rectangular holes in the ground, normally for column base pad foundations. Larger holes may be required for basements etc. Sides may be battered or timbered depending on depth.

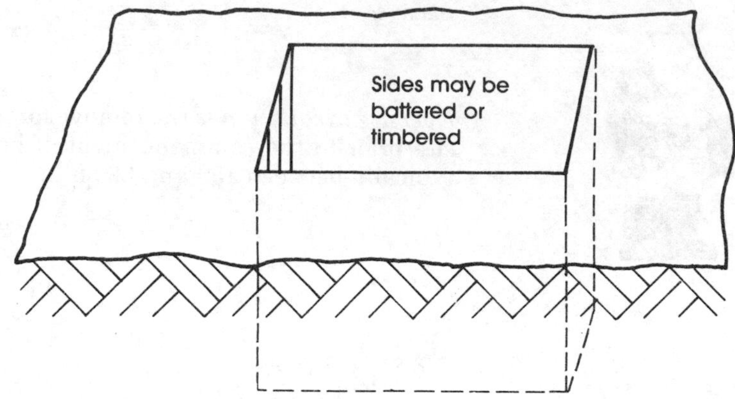

Road construction – in this context the scope is limited to small estate roads, access roads and driveways. Once excavated and scraped down to the formation level construction of the surface can commence on the sub-grade.

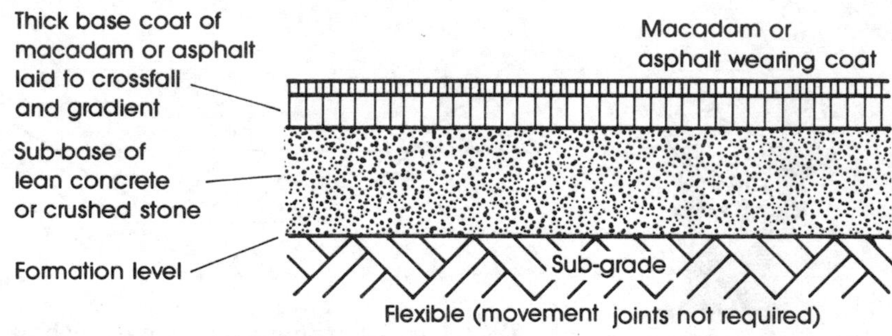

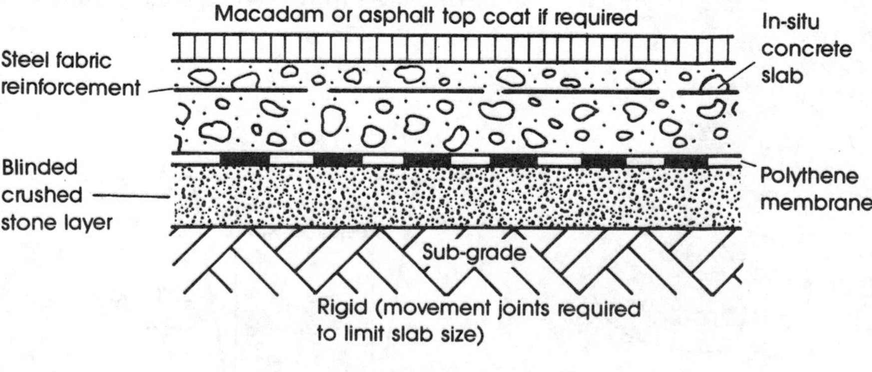

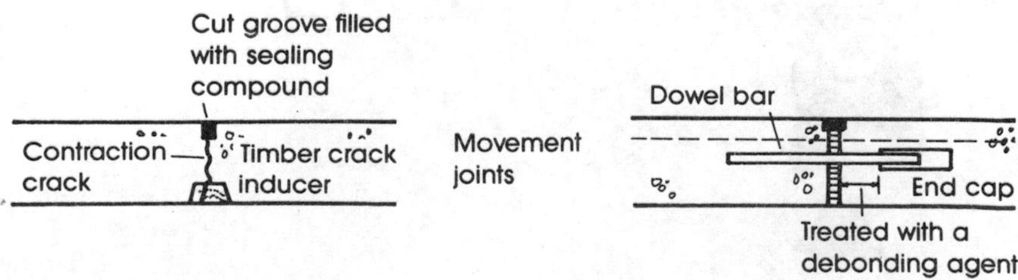

Steel fixing Concrete is very strong when being compressed (squashed) but comparatively weak in tension (stretched). Few structures are subjected to loadings which are totally compressive. Thus steel reinforcement is normally introduced to increase strength and prevent structural failure, thereby producing a composite material called reinforced concrete.

Plain Deformed Twisted Mesh fabric

Shape	Code	Type
	20	Straight
	32	Hook end
	34	Straight turned up one end
	35	Turned up both ends
	41	Cranked for shear
	42	Inclined shear
	60	Stirrups or links

Typical standard shape codes

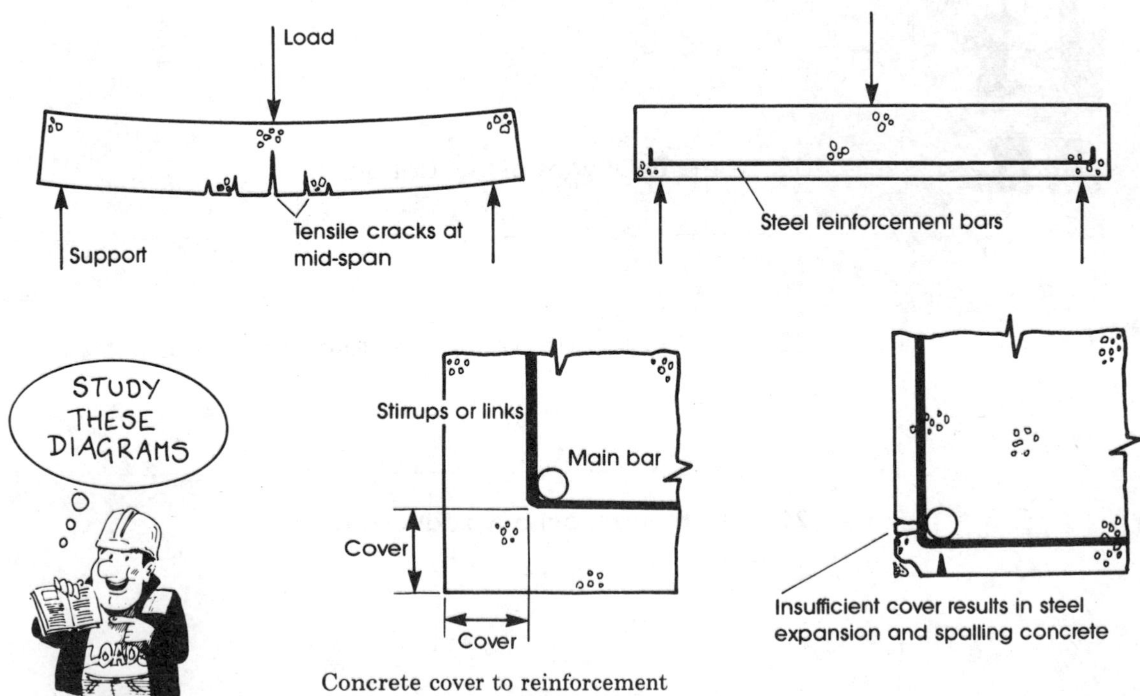

Concrete cover to reinforcement

Formwork – a structure which is usually temporary but can be partly or wholly permanent, designed to contain fresh, fluid concrete, form it into the required shape and dimension and support it until it cures (hardens)

sufficiently to become self-supporting. The surface in contact with the concrete is known as the form face whilst the supporting structure can be referred to as forcework.

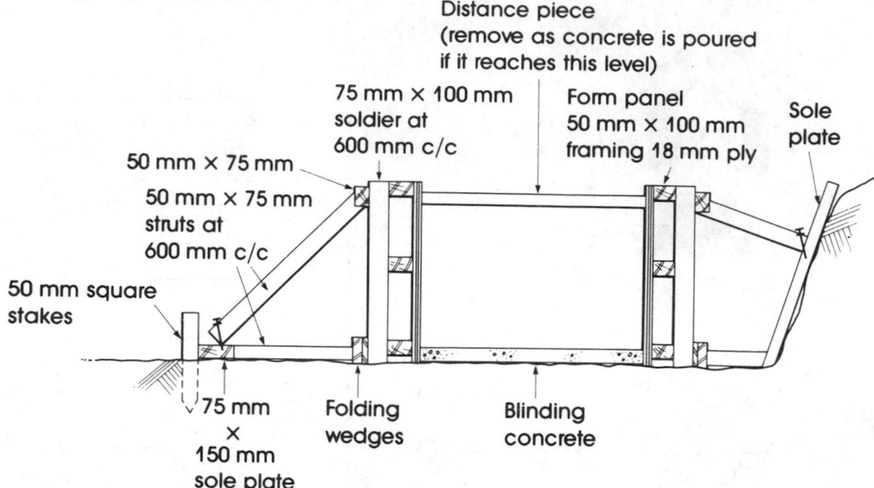

Column pad base formwork

Questions for you

18. Sketch **TWO** types of building structure.

19. Name **TWO** types of foundation.

20. State the purpose of steel reinforcement in concrete.

21. Sketch and label a typical cavity wall.

22. Sketch and label a typical timber upper floor construction.

23. State the purpose of formwork.

24. Name **TWO** methods of excavation.

25. List **FOUR** finishing elements.

26. State two types of road surface.

27. Name any *six* of the lettered features shown.

WORD-SQUARE SEARCH

Hidden in the word square are the following 20 words associated with '*The Construction Industry*'. You may find the words written forwards, backwards, up, down or diagonally.

Public sector	Carpenter
Services	Component
Wall	Formwork
Architect	Floors
Foundation	Tiler
Engineer	Window
Ganger	Restoration
New	Excavation
Surveyor	Roof
Substructure	Element

Draw a ring around the words, or line in using a highlight pen thus:

EXAMPLE

EXAMPLE

2 Health and safety

Accidents

Definition

An accident is often described as a chance event or an unintentional act. This description is not acceptable as accidents do not 'just happen', they do not 'come out of the blue', they are caused! A better definition of an accident is therefore:

An accident is an event causing injury or damage that could have been avoided by following correct methods and procedures.

Accident statistics

Each year there are some 40 000 accidents reported to the Health and Safety Executive which occur during building related activities in Great Britain. Reported accidents are those which result in death, major injury, more than three day's absence from work, or are caused by a notifiable dangerous occurrence. That works out at about 800 accidents each week, 160 accidents each working day, 20 accidents each working hour or one accident every three minutes.

That is, during the time it has taken you to read this far into 'Accidents', somewhere in Great Britain an accident, possibly fatal, has occurred during a building activity, which will be reported to the Health and Safety Executive. Annually, about 140 prove to be fatal. That is almost three deaths each week.

Note: These figures are not intended to frighten you or put you off a future career in the building industry, but simply to make you aware of the hazards involved.

The Health and Safety Executive further break down these reported accident figures into the type of accident and the occupations of those involved.

Causes of accidents

The following illustrations show information about fatal accidents. More than 50 per cent of the accidents involved falls of persons. The reported accidents are classified by occupation: carpenters and joiners are the group most at risk with nearly 11 per cent of the total.

=

=

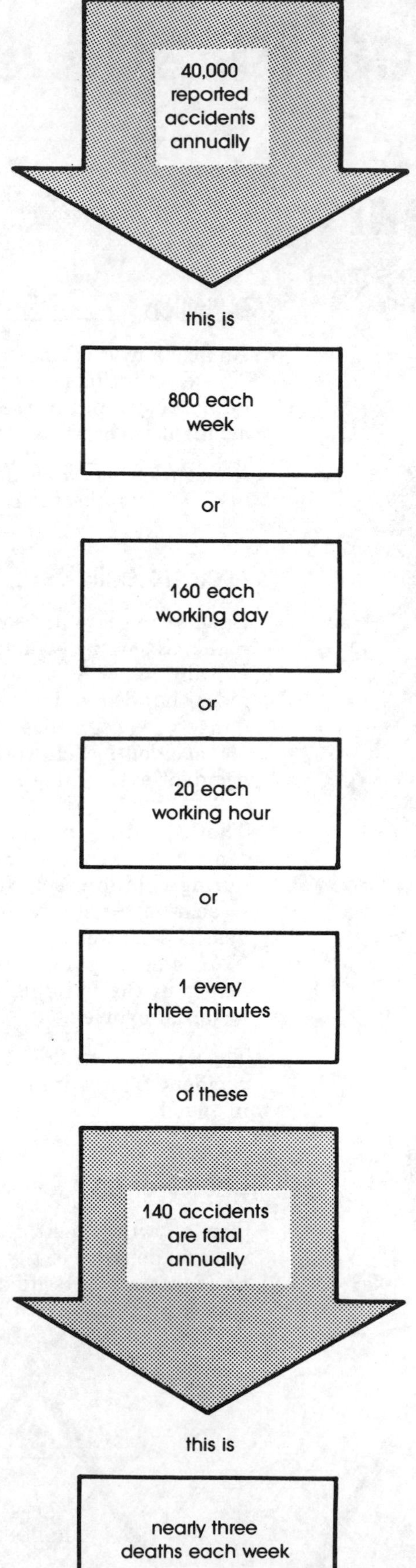

Reported accidents

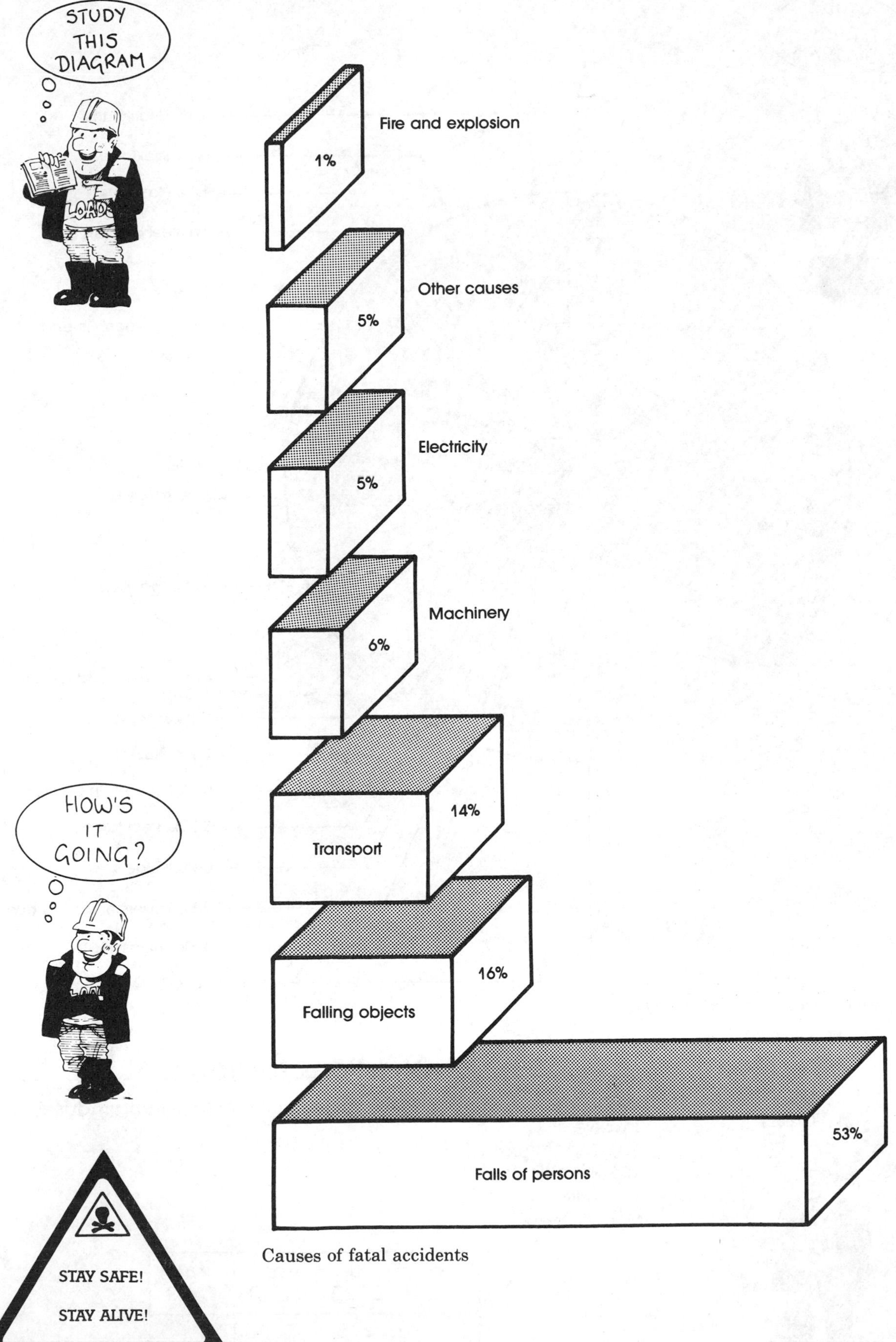

Causes of fatal accidents

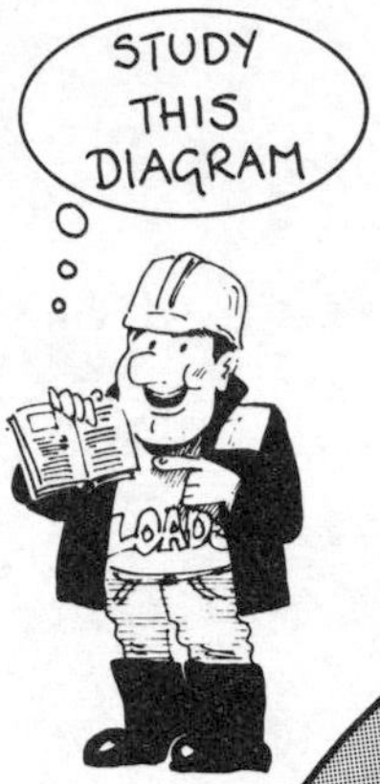

STUDY THIS DIAGRAM

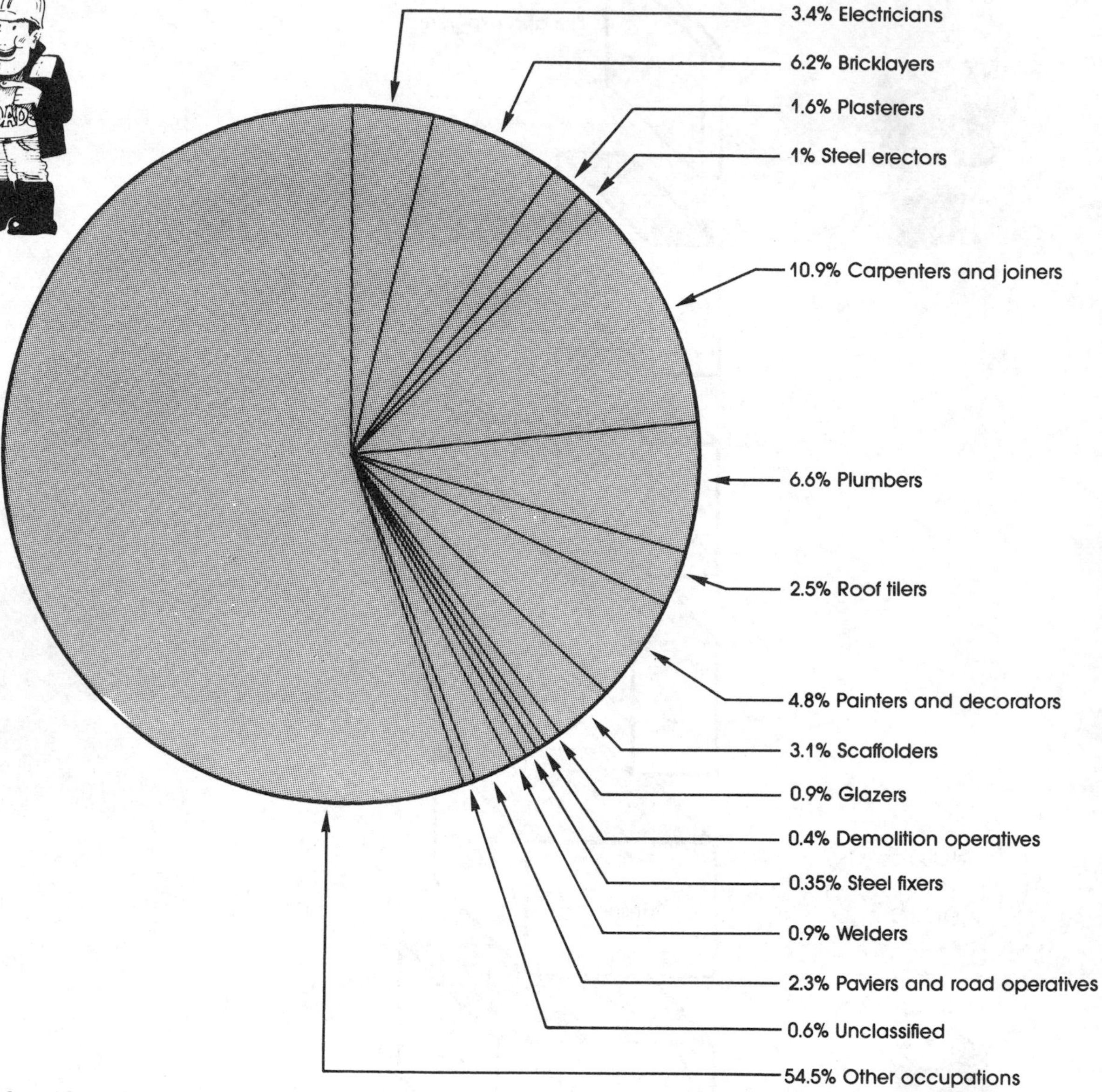

3.4% Electricians
6.2% Bricklayers
1.6% Plasterers
1% Steel erectors
10.9% Carpenters and joiners
6.6% Plumbers
2.5% Roof tilers
4.8% Painters and decorators
3.1% Scaffolders
0.9% Glazers
0.4% Demolition operatives
0.35% Steel fixers
0.9% Welders
2.3% Paviers and road operatives
0.6% Unclassified
54.5% Other occupations

Reported accidents by occupation

Questions for you

1. Over 50 per cent of fatal accidents in the building industry involve:
(a) machinery
(b) electric shock
(c) falls
(d) transport

a	b	c	d
[ ]	[ ]	[ ]	[ ]

2. Define the term 'accident'.

____

____

____

____

____

____

3. Define what constitutes a reported accident and state to whom it is reported.

____

____

____

____

____

____

Safety Check Card

1. ON JOINING THE COMPANY

Have you....

- discussed your previous safety training/experience (if any) with your employer?
  Safety courses attended - certificates.
- read the company safety policy and had the safety organisation explained?
  Safety policy explains company's aims and specifies persons with overall responsibility for safety.
- been shown the safety rules and received instruction in safety procedures?
  Fire, Accidents/First Aid, Transport/Plant, Electricity.
- been given the name and location of the Safety Adviser.?
  Additional details will be given on site.
- been informed of the need to use protective clothing and equipment?
  Operations for which protective clothing and equipment is required.
- been told of your personal responsibilities for health and safety?
  Safety awareness - Safe methods of work.
- had explained the authorisation necessary for the use of plant, machinery, powered hand tools?
  Use of these items restricted to trained persons only.
- been told the need to report 'near misses' and defective plant and equipment?
  Your action may prevent future accidents or dangerous incidents.
- been told of the company's procedure for dealing with grievances and disputes affecting health, safety and welfare?
  Consult with Supervisor or Safety Representative.
- been told or shown where notices relating to safety matters are displayed?
  Safety information displayed on notice board, Safety Bulletins.

....if not, ASK

FTR 007/A

Safety Check Card

2. FOR EMPLOYEES ON SITE

Do you know....

- the hazard areas where risk of injury exists?
  Fragile roofs, excavations, electricity, etc.
- the location of first aid and the person in charge?
  Your nearest first aid box. Name of trained first aider.
- when and where safety helmets must be worn?
  The need to wear, avoiding risk of head injury.
- what to do in the event of fire?
  Means of raising alarm - where the fire extinguishers are, how you operate them. Location of the fire assembly point.
- what to do if you have an accident?
  Obtain first aid treatment. Report it, ensure entry in Accident Book.
- what type of protective clothing and equipment is required or available and how to obtain it?
  How to use and look after it. Where it is issued.
- your responsibility towards good housekeeping?
  Site tidiness, disposal of materials.
- what type of plant and equipment you are not permitted to use?
  All items upon which restriction of use is placed. Examples: Dumpers, fork lifts, woodworking machines.
- the instructions regarding the use of scaffolding and other means of access?
  Scaffolding - necessity for guard rails, toeboards, non-removal of ties, use of brick guards. Ladders - serviceability, security, safe use. Mobile towers and their use.
- your responsibility to report defective plant and equipment, unsafe practices and methods of work?
  Serviceability of plant/equipment, and safe systems of work help prevent accidents.
- the location of all welfare facilities?
  Canteen, washroom and toilets, drying room.

...if in doubt, ASK YOUR SUPERVISOR

Health and safety controls

In 1974 the Health and Safety at Work Act (HASAWA) was introduced. This Act is the main statutory legislation, an enabling umbrella completely covering the health and safety of all persons at their place of work and protecting other people from risks occurring through work activities. All of the existing health and safety requirements operate in parallel with the HASAWA until they are gradually replaced by new regulations and codes of practice etc. made under the Act. The main health and safety legislation applicable to building sites and workshops is indicated in **Table 1**.

=

=

Table 1 Health and safety legislation

Acts of Parliament	*Regulations*
Control Of Pollution Act 1974	
Explosives Act 1875 and 1923	
Factories Act 1961	Abrasive Wheels Regulations 1970 Asbestos Regulations 1969 Construction (General Provision) Regulations 1961 Construction (Lifting Operations) Regulations 1961 Construction (Health and Welfare) Regulations 1966 Construction (Working Places) Regulations 1966 Construction (Head Protection) Regulations 1989 Diving Operations Special Regulations 1960 Electricity (Factories Act) Special Regulations 1908 and 1944

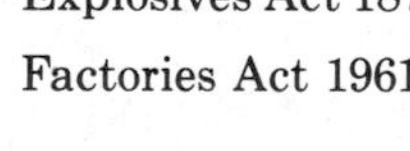

(continued on next page)

Acts of Parliament	*Regulations*
	Highly Flammable Liquids and Liquefied Petroleum Gases Regulations 1972 Lead Paint Regulations 1927 Protection of Eyes Regulations 1974 Woodworking Machines Regulations 1974 Work in Compressed Air Special Regulations 1958 and 1960
Fire Precautions Act 1971	Fire Certificates (Special Premises) Regulations 1976
Food and Drugs Act 1955	Food Hygiene (General) Regulations 1970
Health and Safety at Work Act 1974	Hazardous Substances (Labelling of Road Tankers) Regulations 1978 Control of Lead at Work Regulations 1980 Safety Signs Regulations 1980 Health and Safety (First Aid) Regulations 1981 Control of Asbestos at Work Regulations 1987 Control of Substances Hazardous to Health Regulations 1988 (COSHH) Reporting of Injuries, Diseases and Dangerous Occurences Regulations 1985 (RIDDOR)
Mines and Quarries Act 1954	
Offices, Shops and Railway Premises Act 1963	

HASAWA objectives

The four main objectives of the HASAWA are as follows:

1) To secure the health, safety and welfare of all persons at work.
2) To protect the general public from risks to health and safety arising out of work activities.
3) To control the use, handling, storage and transportation of explosives and highly flammable substances.
4) To control the release of noxious or offensive substances into the atmosphere.

These objectives can be achieved only by involving everyone in health and safety matters. This includes:

- Employers and management
- Employees (and those undergoing training)
- Self-employed
- Designers, manufacturers and suppliers of equipment and materials

Employers' and management duties

Employers have a general duty to ensure the health and safety of their employees, visitors and the general public. This means that the employer must:

1) Provide and maintain a safe working environment.
2) Ensure safe access to and from the workplace.
3) Provide and maintain safe machinery, equipment and methods of work.
4) Ensure the safe handling, transport and storage of all machinery, equipment and materials.
5) Provide their employees with the necessary information, instruction, training and supervision to ensure safe working.
6) Prepare, issue to employees and update as required a written statement of the firm's safety policy.

7) Involve trade union safety representatives (where appointed) with all matters concerning the development, promotion and maintenance of health and safety requirements.

Note: An employer is not allowed to charge an employee for anything done, or any equipment provided, to comply with any health and safety requirement.

Employees' duties

An employee is an individual who offers his or her skill and experience etc. to his or her employer in return for a monetary payment. It is the duty of all employees while at work to comply with the following:

1) Take care at all times and ensure that their actions do not put at 'risk' themselves, their workmates or any other person.
2) Co-operate with their employers to enable them to fulfil the employers' health and safety duties.
3) Use the equipment and safeguards provided by the employers.
4) Never misuse or interfere with anything provided for health and safety.

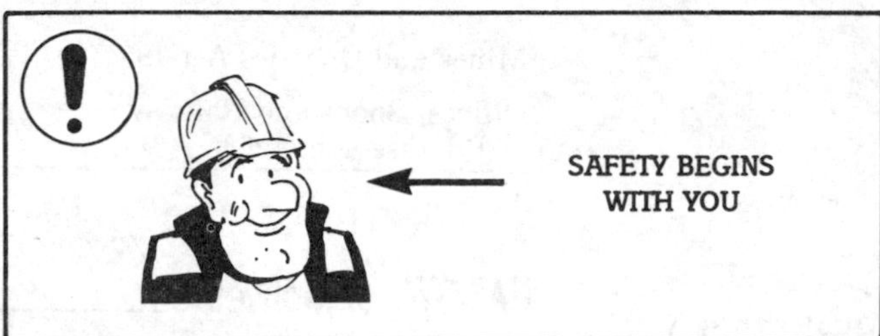

Self-employed duties

The self-employed person can be thought of as both the employer and employee; therefore their duties under the Act are a combination of those of the employer and employee.

Designers', manufacturers' and suppliers' duties

Under the Act, designers, manufacturers and suppliers as well as importers and hirers of equipment, machinery and materials for use at work have a duty to:

1) Ensure that the equipment machinery or material is designed, manufactured and tested so that when it is used correctly no hazard to health and safety is created.
2) Provide information or operating instructions as to the correct use, without risk, of their equipment, machinery or material.
   Note: Employers should ensure this information is passed on to their employees.
3) Carry out research so that any risk to health and safety is eliminated or minimised as far as possible.

Enforcement

Under the HASAWA a system of control was established, aimed at reducing death, injury and ill-health. This system of control consists of the Health and Safety Executive (HSE). The Executive is divided into a number of specialist inspectorates or sections which operate from local offices situated throughout the country. From the local office, inspectors visit individual workplaces.

Note: The section with the main responsibility for the building industry is the Factory Inspectorate.

The Health and Safety Executive inspectors have been given wide powers of entry, examination and investigation in order to assist them in the enforcement of the HASAWA and earlier safety legislation. In addition to giving employers advice and information on health and safety matters, an inspector can do the following:

1) *Enter premises* in order to carry out investigations, including the taking of measurements, photographs, recordings and samples. The inspector may require the premises to be left undisturbed while the investigations are taking place.
2) *Take statements* An inspector can ask anyone questions relevant to the investigation and also require them to sign a declaration as to the truth of the answers.
3) *Check records* All books, records and documents required by legislation must be made available for inspection and copying.
4) *Give information* An inspector has a duty to give employees or their safety representative information about the safety of their workplace and details of any action he/she proposes to take. This information must also be given to the employer.
5) *Demand* The inspector can demand the seizure, dismantling, neutralising or destruction of any machinery, equipment, material or substance that is likely to cause immediate serious personal injury.
6) *Issue an improvement notice* This requires the responsible person (employer or manufacturer etc.) to put right within a specified period of time any minor hazard or infringement of legislation.
7) *Issue a prohibition notice* This requires the responsible person to stop immediately any activities which are likely to result in serious personal injury. This ban on activities continues until the situation is corrected. An appeal against an improvement or prohibition notice may be made to an industrial tribunal.
8) *Prosecute* All persons, including employers, employees, self-employed, designers, manufacturers and suppliers who fail to comply with their safety duty may be prosecuted in a magistrates' court or in certain circumstances in the higher court system. Conviction can lead to unlimited fines, or a prison sentence, or both.

BUILDING AND CONSTRUCTION

SAFETY NEWS. June. PSB

Harry Whiteman is Safety Consultant to BBS Contracts

Maidstone Crown Court fined a building contractor £25 000 recently over an incident where an 18-year-old trainee lost both hands and feet when the scaffold tube he was unloading touched an overhead 33 000 volt electric cable. The Health and Safety Executive had asked in the magistrates court, where the maximum penalty is £2000, for this case to be referred to the Crown Court for sentence.

A major contractor in Birmingham city centre was recently fined £500 for supplying only two safety helmets for the 20 people who were employed on-site.

A 22-year-old site operative who lost the sight in one eye as a result of a grinding wheel accident, was fined £250 in Northampton Magistrates' Court this week. The Health and Safety Executive who brought the prosecution claimed that the operative had failed to take notice of the safety sign or wear the safety goggles which had been supplied by the employer.

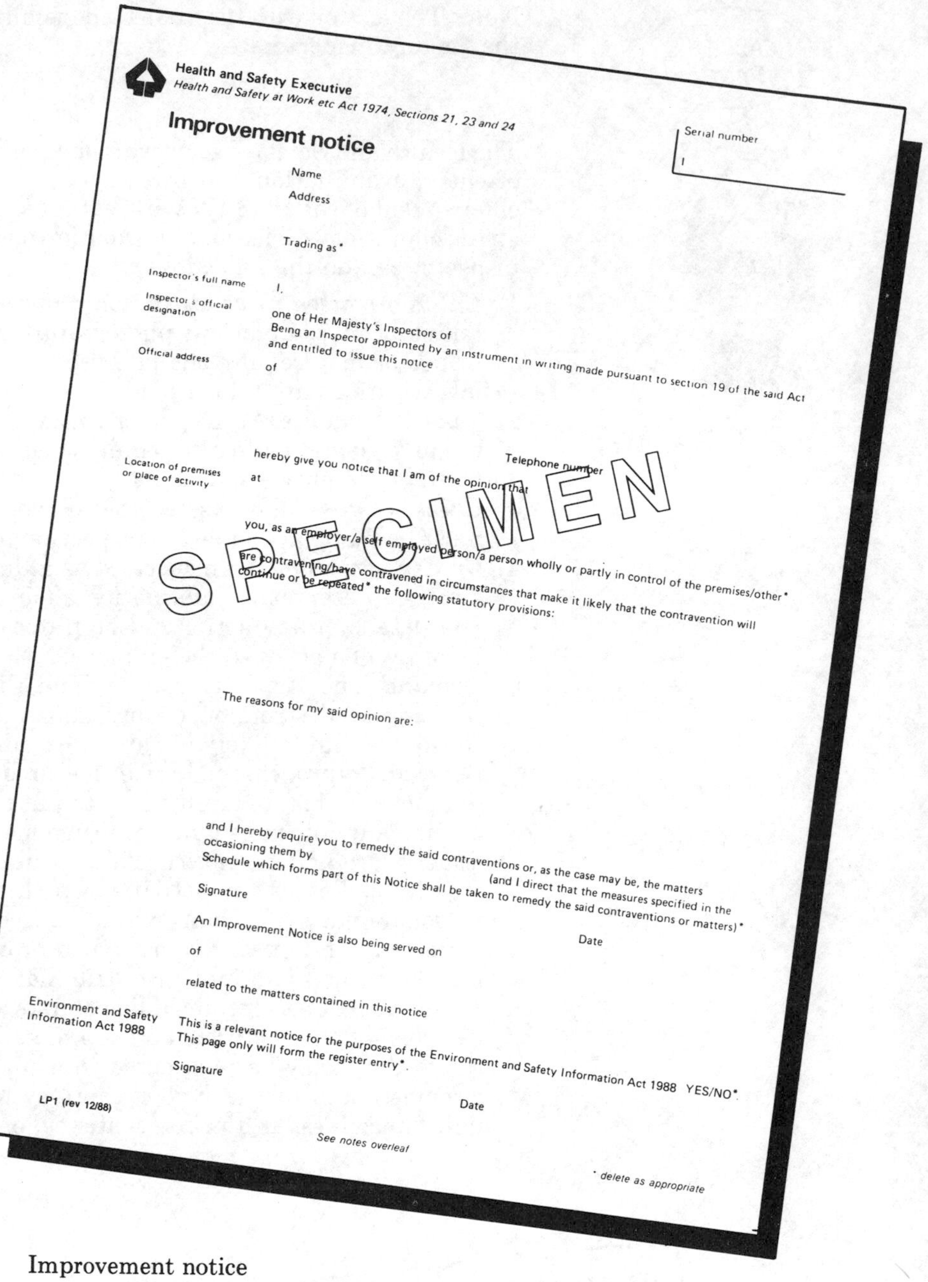

Health and Safety Executive
Health and Safety at Work etc Act 1974, Sections 21, 23 and 24

Improvement notice

Serial number I

Name
Address

Trading as*

Inspector's full name: I,

Inspector's official designation: one of Her Majesty's Inspectors of

Being an Inspector appointed by an instrument in writing made pursuant to section 19 of the said Act and entitled to issue this notice

Official address: of

Telephone number

hereby give you notice that I am of the opinion that

Location of premises or place of activity: at

you, as an employer/a self employed person/a person wholly or partly in control of the premises/other*

are contravening/have contravened in circumstances that make it likely that the contravention will continue or be repeated* the following statutory provisions:

SPECIMEN

The reasons for my said opinion are:

and I hereby require you to remedy the said contraventions or, as the case may be, the matters occasioning them by (and I direct that the measures specified in the Schedule which forms part of this Notice shall be taken to remedy the said contraventions or matters)*

Signature Date

An Improvement Notice is also being served on

of

related to the matters contained in this notice

Environment and Safety Information Act 1988: This is a relevant notice for the purposes of the Environment and Safety Information Act 1988 YES/NO*.
This page only will form the register entry*.

Signature Date

LP1 (rev 12/88)

See notes overleaf

** delete as appropriate*

Improvement notice

Questions for you

4. State **TWO** of the main objectives of the Health and Safety at Work Act.

5. State TWO duties of each of the following under the Health and Safety at Work Act.
(a) Employers
(b) Employees

(a) ______________________________

(b) ______________________________

6. State THREE main powers of a Health and Safety Executive inspector.

____

____

____

WORK THROUGH THE SECTION AGAIN IF YOU HAD ANY PROBLEMS

Health and Safety Executive
Health and Safety at Work etc Act 1974, Sections 22, 23 and 24

Serial Number
P

Prohibition notice

Name

Address

Trading as*

Inspector's full name — I,

Inspector's official designation — one of Her Majesty's Inspectors of
Being an Inspector appointed by an instrument in writing made pursuant to section 19 of the said Act and entitled to issue this notice

Official address — of

Telephone number

hereby give you notice that I am of the opinion that the following activities namely:

Location of premises or place of activity — which are being carried on by you/ likely to be carried on by you/under your control* at

involve, or will involve, a risk of serious personal injury, and that the matters which give rise / will give rise* to the said risk (s) are:

SPECIMEN

and that the said matters involve / will involve* contravention of the following statutory provisions:

because

and I hereby direct that the said activities shall not be carried on by you or under your control immediately/after* unless the said contravention(s)* and matters have been remedied.

I further direct that the measures specified in the schedule which forms part of this notice shall be taken to remedy the said contravention(s)* or matters.*

Signature

Date

* A Prohibition Notice is also being served on

of

related to the matters contained in this notice

Environment and Safety Information Act 1988 — This is a relevant notice for the purposes of the Environment and Safety Information Act 1988 YES/NO*.
This page only will form the register entry*.

Signature

Date

LP2 (rev 12/88)

See notes overleaf

**delete as appropriate*

Prohibition notice

The construction regulations

These are the regulations made under the Factories Act 1961 which are specific to construction operations. They are divided into four parts, each dealing with a different aspect of work.

Construction (General Provisions) Regulations 1961 set out minimum standards to promote a good level of general safety.

Construction (Lifting Operations) Regulations 1961 lay down requirements regarding the manufacture, maintenance and inspection of lifting appliances used on site (gin wheels, cranes and hoists, etc.).

Construction (Health and Welfare) Regulations 1966 set out minimum provisions for site accommodation, washing facilities, sanitary conveniences and protective clothing. See **Table 2** 'Safety, health and welfare on site'.

Construction (Working Places) Regulations 1966 control the erection, use and inspection of scaffolds and other similar temporary structures.

Construction (Head Protection) Regulations 1989 place a duty on employers to provide and ensure that suitable head protection is worn on site. Employees and the self-employed are obliged to wear it when instructed to do so.

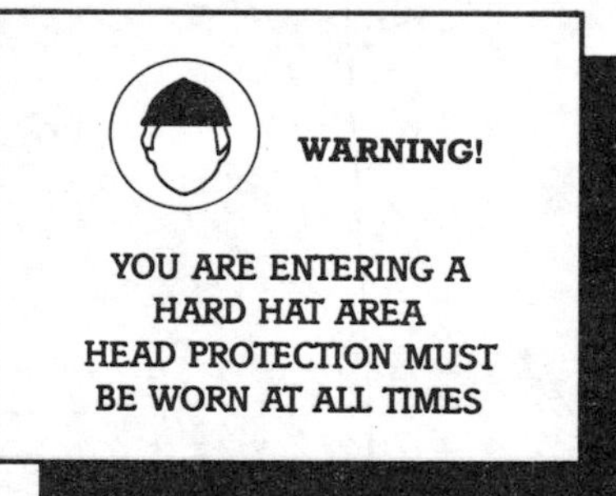

Table 2 Safety, health and welfare on site

Type of site/number of people on site	*What must be provided*
Every site	A clean and orderly place in which to shelter during bad weather A means of keeping warm A place to sit when eating A means of boiling water A supply of drinking water A place to store and dry work clothing A place to store personal clothing Washing facilities Toilets and urinals, clean, under cover with lockable door and lighting to be provided. Separate facilities are required for men and women, a minimum of one for every 25 persons Protective clothing to be provided if expected to work in poor weather conditions An appointed person responsible for the first aid box and summoning medical attention* A first aid box. Travelling first aid kits should be provided for those on the move or when working alone or in small groups in isolated locations*

(continued on next page)

Type of site/number of people on site	*What must be provided*
When using lead or poisonous substances	Nail brushes, soap, towel or dryer, hot and cold or warm water, wash basin or bucket for every 5 or part of 5 persons
More than 5	Heating and drying arrangements must be adequate and suitable
More than 10	Hot food available or a means of heating one's own
20 or more	A wash basin, soap, towel or dryer, hot and cold or warm water to be provided where work is expected to last more than 6 weeks
More than 50	A person properly trained and recently certificated in first aid procedures*
More than 100	A minimum of 4 wash basins and an additional one for every 35 or part of 35 persons above 100 and an adequate supply of soap, towels or dryer, hot and cold or warm water to be provided where the work is unlikely to be completed within 12 months. Additional toilet facilities, one for every 35 or part of 35 persons above 100

Note: Where the site has fewer than 5 personnel the heating and drying arrangements must be provided where reasonably practicable. Items * are required by the Health and Safety (First Aid) Regulations 1981

Safety documentation

In order to comply with the various safety legislation, an employer is required to:

- Display notices and certificates
- Notify relevant authorities
- Keep relevant records

Notices and certificates

An employer must prominently display on site, in the workshop, or in an office where the employees attend, a number of notices and certificates, the main ones being (where applicable):

1) Copy of the certificate of insurance; this is required under the Employers' Liability (Compulsory Insurance) Act 1969.
2) Copy of fire certificate.
3) Abstract of the Factories Act 1961 for building operations and works of engineering constructions.
4) Details of the area Health and Safety Executive Inspectorate; the employment medical adviser and the site safety supervisor should be indicated on this form.
5) Abstract of the Offices, Shops and Railway Premises Act 1963.
6) The Woodworking Machines Regulations 1974.
7) The Abrasive Wheels Regulations 1970 and cautionary notice.
8) The Electricity (Factories Act) Special Regulations 1908 and 1944. Electric shock (first aid) placard.
9) The Asbestos Regulations 1969.
10) The Highly Flammable Liquids and Liquefied Petroleum Gases Regulations 1972.

Notifications

The following are the main notifications required. They are usually submitted on standard forms obtainable from the relevant authority.

1) The commencement of building operations or works of engineering constructions that are likely to last more than six weeks.
2) The employment of persons in an office or shop for more than 21 hours a week.
3) The employment or transfer of young persons (under 18 years of age) must be notified to the local careers office.
4) Accidents resulting in death or major injuries or notifiable dangerous occurrences, or more than three days absence from work. Major injuries

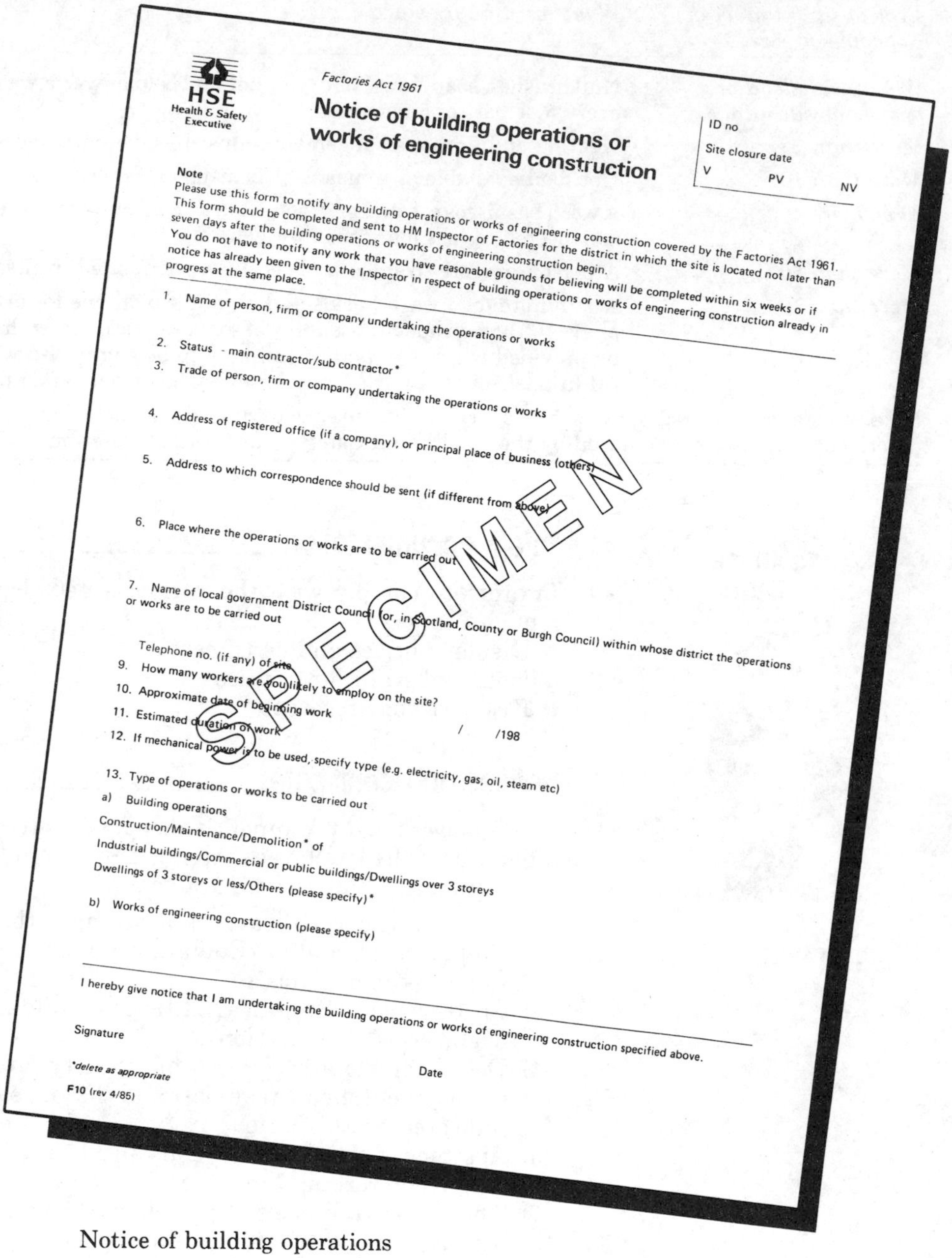

HSE Health & Safety Executive

Factories Act 1961

Notice of building operations or works of engineering construction

ID no
Site closure date
V PV NV

Note
Please use this form to notify any building operations or works of engineering construction covered by the Factories Act 1961.
This form should be completed and sent to HM Inspector of Factories for the district in which the site is located not later than seven days after the building operations or works of engineering construction begin.
You do not have to notify any work that you have reasonable grounds for believing will be completed within six weeks or if notice has already been given to the Inspector in respect of building operations or works of engineering construction already in progress at the same place.

1. Name of person, firm or company undertaking the operations or works
2. Status - main contractor/sub contractor*
3. Trade of person, firm or company undertaking the operations or works
4. Address of registered office (if a company), or principal place of business (others)
5. Address to which correspondence should be sent (if different from above)
6. Place where the operations or works are to be carried out
7. Name of local government District Council (or, in Scotland, County or Burgh Council) within whose district the operations or works are to be carried out

Telephone no. (if any) of site
9. How many workers are you likely to employ on the site?
10. Approximate date of beginning work / /198
11. Estimated duration of work
12. If mechanical power is to be used, specify type (e.g. electricity, gas, oil, steam etc)
13. Type of operations or works to be carried out
a) Building operations
Construction/Maintenance/Demolition* of
Industrial buildings/Commercial or public buildings/Dwellings over 3 storeys
Dwellings of 3 storeys or less/Others (please specify)*
b) Works of engineering construction (please specify)

I hereby give notice that I am undertaking the building operations or works of engineering construction specified above.

Signature

Date

*delete as appropriate

F10 (rev 4/85)

SPECIMEN

Notice of building operations

can be defined as most fractures, amputations, loss of sight or any other injury involving a stay in hospital. Many incidents can be defined as notifiable dangerous occurrences but in general they include the collapse of a crane, hoist, scaffolding or building, an explosion or fire, or the escape of any substance that is liable to cause a health hazard or major injury to any person.

5) A poisoning or suffocation incident resulting in acute ill-health requiring medical treatment.
6) Application for a fire certificate, if required under the Fire Certificates (Special Premises) Regulations 1976.

STUDY AND FILL IN THIS FORM

ASSUME A SITUATION

Health and Safety Executive
Health and Safety at Work etc Act 1974
Reporting of Injuries, Diseases and Dangerous Occurrences Regulations 1985

Spaces below are for office use only

Report of an injury or dangerous occurrence

- Full notes to help you complete this form are attached.
- This form is to be used to make a report to the enforcing authority under the requirements of Regulations 3 or 6.
- Completing and signing this form does not constitute an admission of liability of any kind, either by the person making the report or any other person.
- If more than one person was injured as a result of an accident, please complete a separate form for each person.

A Subject of report *(tick appropriate box or boxes) – see note 2*

Fatality ☐ 1 | Specified major injury or condition ☐ 2 | "Over three day" injury ☐ 3 | Dangerous occurrence ☐ 4 | Flammable gas incident (fatality or major injury or condition) ☐ 5 | Dangerous gas fitting ☐ 6

B Person or organisation making report (ie person obliged to report under the Regulations) *– see note 3*

Name and address –

Post code –

Name and telephone no. of person to contact –

Nature of trade, business or undertaking –

If in construction industry, state the total number of your employees –

and indicate the role of your company on site *(tick box)* –

Main site contractor ☐ 7 | Sub contractor ☐ 8 | Other ☐ 9

If in farming, are you reporting an injury to a member of your family? *(tick box)* Yes ☐ No ☐

SPECIMEN

C Date, time and place of accident, dangerous occurrence or flammable gas incident *– see note 4*

Date ☐☐ 19☐ (*day month year*) Time –

Give the name and address if different from above –

Where on the premises or site –
and
Normal activity carried on there

ENV

Complete the following sections D, E, F & H if you have ticked boxes, 1, 2, 3 or 5 in Section A. Otherwise go straight to Sections G and H.

D The injured person *– see note 5*

Full name and address –

Age ☐ Sex ☐ (M or F) Status (*tick box*) –

Employee ☐ 10 | Self employed ☐ 11 | Trainee (YTS) ☐ 12 | Trainee (other) ☐ 13 | Any other person ☐ 14

Trade, occupation or job title –

Nature of injury or condition and the part of the body affected –

F2508 (rev 1/86)

continued overleaf

17

E Kind of accident - *see note 6*

Indicate what kind of accident led to the injury or condition (*tick one box*) –

- Contact with moving machinery or material being machined [ ] 1
- Struck by moving, including flying or falling, object. [ ] 2
- Struck by moving vehicle [ ] 3
- Struck against something fixed or stationary [ ] 4
- Injured whilst handling lifting or carrying [ ] 5
- Slip, trip or fall on same level [ ] 6
- Fall from a height* [ ] 7
- *Distance through which person fell [ ] (metres)
- Trapped by something collapsing or overturning [ ] 8
- Drowning or asphyxiation [ ] 9
- Exposure to or contact with a harmful substance [ ] 10
- Exposure to fire [ ] 11
- Exposure to an explosion [ ] 12
- Contact with electricity or an electrical discharge [ ] 13
- Injured by an animal [ ] 14
- Other kind of accident (give details in Section H) [ ] 15

Spaces below are for office use only [ ]

F Agent(s) involved – *see note 7*

Indicate which, if any, of the categories of agent or factor below were involved (*tick one or more of the boxes*) –

- Machinery/equipment for lifting and conveying [ ] 1
- Portable power or hand tools [ ] 2
- Any vehicle or associated equipment/machinery [ ] 3
- Other machinery [ ] 4
- Process plant, pipework or bulk storage [ ] 5
- Any material, substance or product being handled, used or stored. [ ] 6
- Gas, vapour, dust, fume or oxygen deficient atmosphere [ ] 7
- Pathogen or infected material [ ] 8
- Live animal [ ] 9
- Moveable container or package of any kind [ ] 10
- Floor, ground, stairs or any working surface [ ] 11
- Building, engineering structure or excavation/underground working [ ] 12
- Ladder or scaffolding [ ] 13
- Construction formwork, shuttering and falsework [ ] 14
- Electricity supply cable, wiring, apparatus or equipment [ ] 15
- Entertainment or sporting facilities or equipment [ ] 16
- Any other agent [ ] 17

SPECIMEN

Describe briefly the agents or factors you have indicated –

G Dangerous occurrence or dangerous gas fitting – *see notes 8 and 9*

Reference number of dangerous occurrence [ ]

Reference number of dangerous gas fitting [ ]

H Account of accident, dangerous occurrence or flammable gas incident - *see note 10*

Describe what happened and how. In the case of an accident state what the injured person was doing at the time –

Signature of person making report [ ]

Date [ ]

48 Report of accident (continued)

Records

Employers are required to keep various records. These should be kept ready for inspection on site or at the place of work and should include the following:

1) The general register for building operations and works of engineering constructions. This is used to record details of the site or workshop and the nature of work taking place, any cases of poisoning or disease and the employment or transfer of young persons.
2) An accident book in which details of all accidents are recorded.
3) A record of accidents, dangerous occurrences and ill-health enquiries. Entries in the record must be made whenever the Health and Safety Executive is notified of an accident resulting in death, major injury or a notifiable dangerous occurrence.
4) Register for the purposes of the Abrasive Wheels Regulations 1970. A register used to record details of persons appointed to mount abrasive wheels.

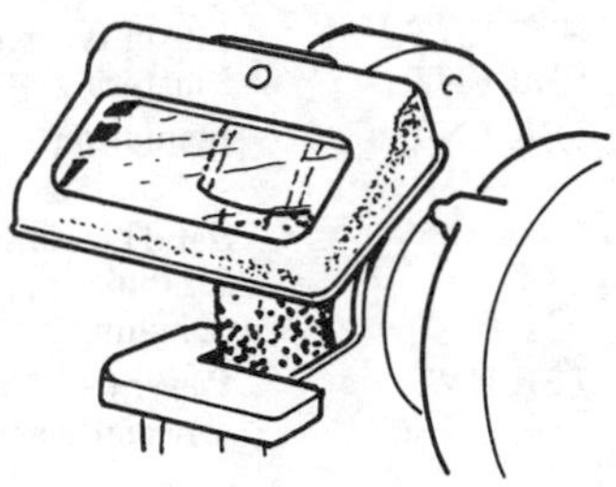

5) Records of inspections, examinations and special tests. This is a booklet of forms on which details of inspections etc. on scaffolding, excavations, earthworks and lifting appliances must be recorded.
6) Record of reports. This provides forms for recording the thorough examination of lifting appliances, hoists, chains, ropes and other lifting gear and also the heat treatment of chains and lifting gear.
7) Register and certificate of shared welfare arrangements. To be completed where an employer, normally the main contractor, provides the welfare facilities for another employer (sub-contractor).
8) Certificates of tests and examinations of various lifting appliances. These are records of the weekly, monthly or other periodic tests and examinations required by the construction regulations as follows:
   cranes
   hoists
   other lifting appliances
   wire and ropes
   chains, slings and lifting gear.

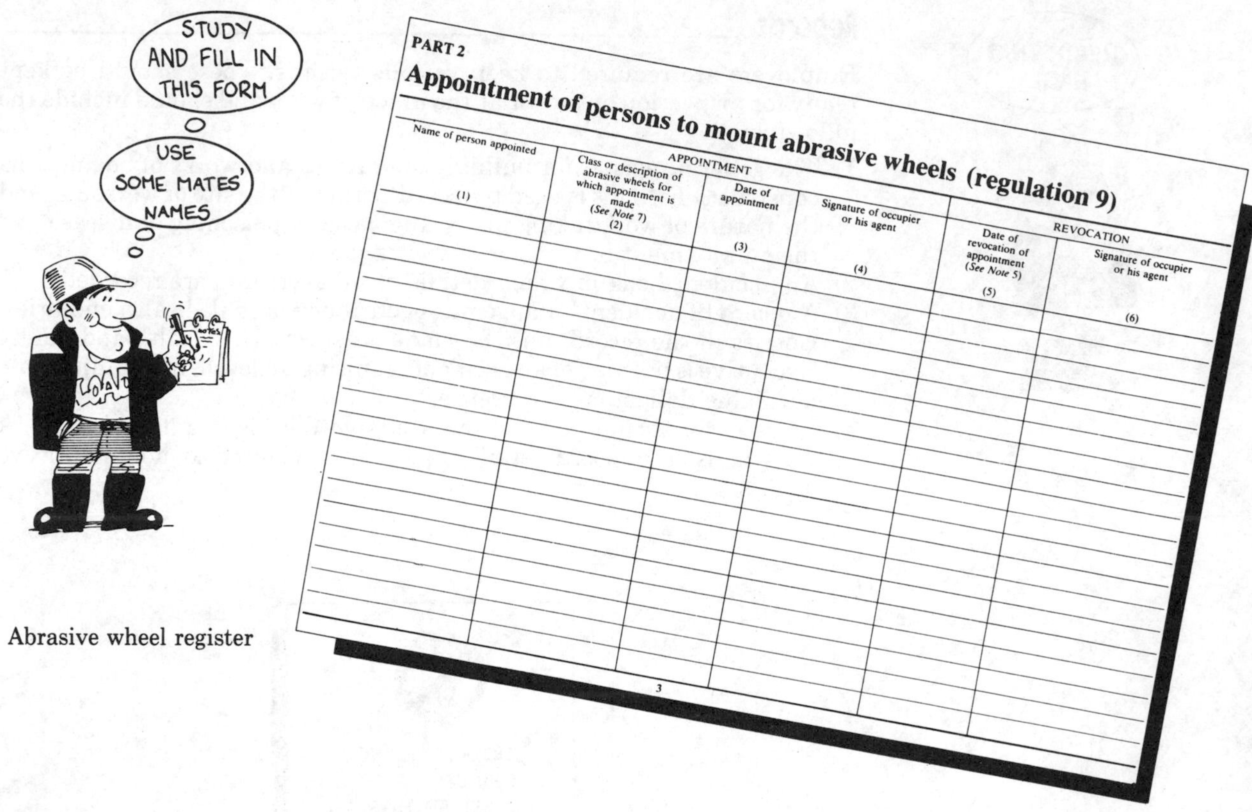

PART 2

Appointment of persons to mount abrasive wheels (regulation 9)

Name of person appointed (1)	APPOINTMENT: Class or description of abrasive wheels for which appointment is made (See Note 7) (2)	Date of appointment (3)	Signature of occupier or his agent (4)	REVOCATION: Date of revocation of appointment (See Note 5) (5)	Signature of occupier or his agent (6)

3

Abrasive wheel register

Hazardous substances in construction

Substances	*Health risk*	*Jobs*	*Controls*
DUSTS:			
Cement (Also when wet)	SK I ENT	Masonry, rendering	Prevent spread. Protective clothing, respirator when handling dry, washing facilities, barrier cream.
Gypsum	SK I ENT	Plastering	
Man-made mineral fibre	I SK ENT	Insulation	Minimise handling/cutting, respirator, one piece overall, gloves, eye protection.
Silica	I	Sand blasting, grit blasting: scrabbling granite, polishing	Substitution — e.g. with grit, silica-free sand; wet methods; process enclosure/extraction; respirator.
Wood dust (Dust from treated timber e.g. with pesticide may present extra hazards)	I SK ENT	Power tool use in carpentry, especially sanding	Off-site preparation; on-site — enclosures with exhaust ventilation; portable tools — dust extraction; washing facilities; respirator.
Mixed dusts (Mineral and biological)	I SK ENT	Demolition and refurbishment	Minimise dust generation; use wet methods where possible; segregate or reduce number of workers exposed; protective clothing, respirator; good washing facilities/showers. Tetanus immunisation.
FUMES/GASES:			
Various welding fumes from metals or rods	I	Welding/cutting activities	Mechanical ventilation in enclosed spaces; air supplied helmet; elsewhere good general ventilation.
Hydrogen sulphide	I ENT	Sewers, drains, excavations, manholes	All work in confined spaces — exhaust and blower ventilation; self contained breathing equipment confined space procedures.
Carbon monoxide/nitrous oxide	I	Plant exhausts	Position away from confined spaces. Where possible maintain exhaust filters; forced ventilation and extraction of fumes.
SOLVENTS: In many construction products — paints, adhesives, strippers, thinners, etc.	I SK SW	Many trades, particularly painting, tile fixing. Spray application is high risk. Most brush/roller work less risk. Regular exposure increases risks	Breathing apparatus for spraying, particularly in enclosed spaces; use of mistless/airless methods. Otherwise ensure good general ventilation. Washing facilities, barrier cream.

(continued on next page)

Substances	*Health risk*	*Jobs*	*Controls*
RESIN SYSTEMS:			
Isocyanates (MDI:TDI)	I ENT SK SW	Thermal insulation	Mechanical ventilation where necessary; respirators; protective clothing, washing facilities. Skin checks, respiratory checks.
Polyurethane paints	I ENT SK SW	Decorative surface coatings	Spraying — airline/self contained breathing apparatus; elsewhere good general ventilation. One piece overall, gloves, washing facilities.
Epoxy	I SK SW	Strong adhesive applications	Good ventilation, personal protective equipment (respirator; clothing) washing facilities, barrier cream.
Polyester	I SK ENT SW	Glass fibre claddings and coatings	As above.
PESTICIDES: (e.g. timber preservatives, fungicides, weed killers)	I SK ENT SW	Particularly in-situ timber treatment. Handling treated timber	Use least toxic material. Mechanical ventilation, respirator, impervious gloves, one piece overall and head cover. In confined spaces — breathing apparatus. Washing facilities, skin checks. If necessary biological checks. Handle only dry material.
ACIDS/ALKALIS:	SK ENT	Masonry cleaning	Use weakest solutions. Protective clothing, eye protection. Washing facilities (first aid including eye bath and copious water for splash removal).
MINERAL OIL:	SK I	Work near machines, compressors, etc. Mould release agents	Filters to reduce mist. Good ventilation. Protective clothing. Washing facilities; barrier creams. Skin checks.
SITE CONTAMINANTS: e.g. Arsenic. Phanols; heavy metals; Micro organisms etc. e.g. Wells disease, tetanus, hepatitis B	I SK SW	Site re-development of industrial premises or hospitals — particularly demolition groundwork and drain/sewers	Thorough site examination and clearance procedures. Respirators, protective clothing. Washing facilities/showers. Immunisation for tetanus.

Health risk
SK = skin; I = inhalation; ENT = irritant eyes, nose, throat; SW = ingestion
Table extracted from Control of Substances Hazardous to Health (COSHH) regulations

SELECT ONE SUBSTANCE/JOB ASSOCIATED WITH YOUR OCCUPATION AND WRITE A MEMO TO A WORKMATE INSTRUCTING THEM ON THE HAZARDS INVOLVED AND THE CORRECT WORK PROCEDURE TO BE UNDERTAKEN

BBS CONSTRUCTION **MEMO**

From ______________________ To ______________________

Subject ______________________ Date ______________________

Message

Questions for you

7. Name THREE notices or certificates that must be displayed on a building site.

____

____

____

____

____

____

8. Name TWO parts of the Construction Regulations.

____

____

____

____

Safety signs

Formerly there were many vastly different safety signs in use. British Standard BS 5378 Part 1, 1980: 'Safety Signs and Colours' introduced a standard system of giving health and safety information with a minimum use of words. Its purpose is to establish an internationally understood system of safety signs and safety colours which draws attention to objects and situations that do, or could, affect health and safety. Details of these signs and typical examples of use are given in **Table 3**.

Stop/ must not

PROHIBITION

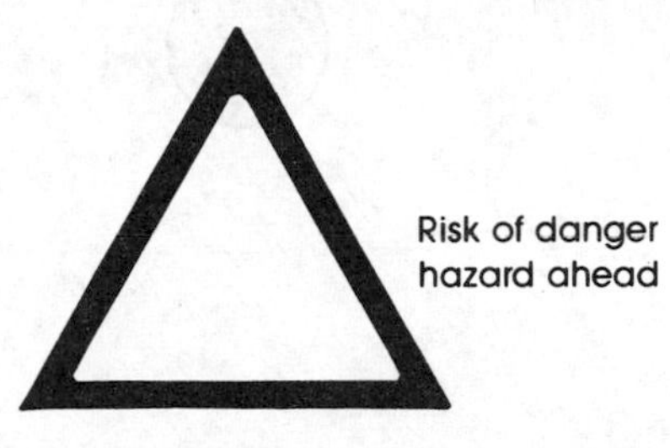

Risk of danger hazard ahead

WARNING

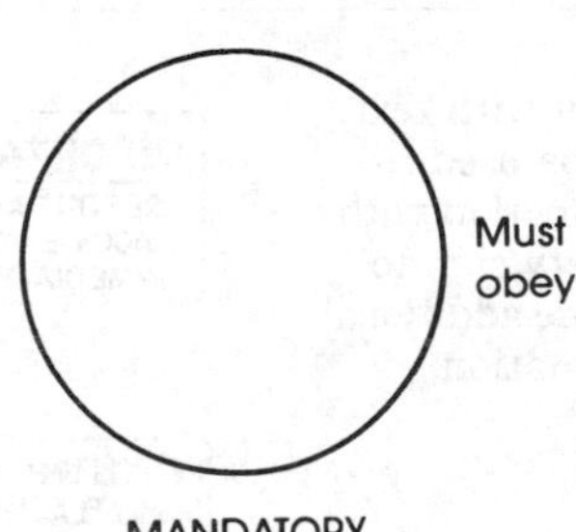

Must obey

MANDATORY

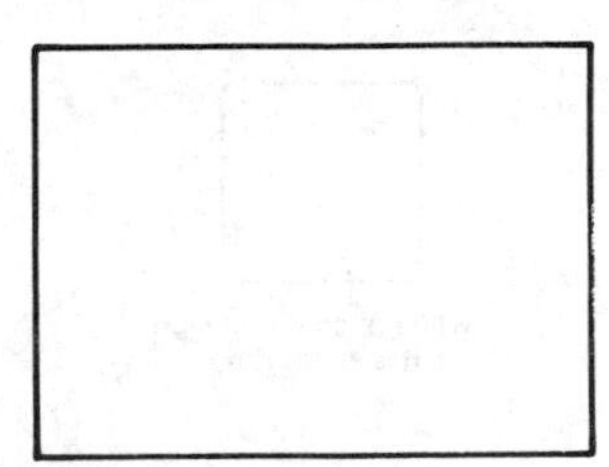

Safe condition

SAFE WAY TO GO

Table 3 Safety signs

Purpose	*Sign*	*Definition*	*Examples for use*
Prohibition	white red 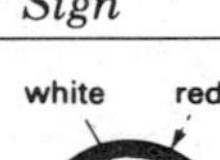	A sign prohibiting certain behaviour	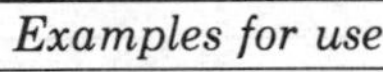  No smoking  Smoking and naked flames prohibited  Do not extinguish with water  Not drinking water  Pedestrians prohibited
Caution 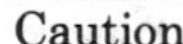	yellow black 	A sign giving warning of certain hazards	 Caution, risk of fire  Caution, toxic hazard  Caution, corrosive substance  General warning caution, risk of danger  Caution, risk of electric shock  Perimeter of hazard

(continued overleaf)

Purpose	*Sign*	*Definition*	*Examples for use*
Safe condition	green	A sign providing information about safe conditions	First aid; Indication of direction; Indication of direction
Mandatory	blue	A sign indicating that a special course of action is required	Head protection must be worn; Eye protection must be worn; Hearing protection must be worn; Foot protection must be worn; Hand protection must be worn; Respiratory protection must be worn
Supplementary	white or colour of sign it is supporting	A sign with text. Can be used in conjunction with a safety sign to provide additional information.	IMPORTANT REPORT ALL ACCIDENTS IMMEDIATELY; SCAFFOLDING INCOMPLETE; SAFETY HELMETS ARE PROVIDED FOR YOUR SAFETY AND MUST BE WORN; PETROLEUM MIXURE HIGHLY FLAMMABLE NO SMOKING OR NAKED LIGHTS; WARNING HIGH VOLTAGE CABLES OVERHEAD; EYE WASH BOTTLE

Questions for you

9. A safety sign that is contained in a yellow triangle with a black border is:
(a) prohibiting certain behaviour
(b) warning of certain hazards
(c) providing information about safety
(d) indicating that safety equipment must be worn.

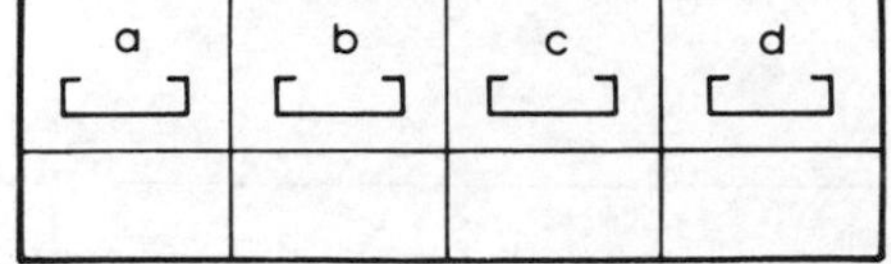

General safety

It should be the aim of everyone to prevent accidents. Remember, you are required by law to be aware and fulfil your duties under the Health and Safety at Work Act.

The main contribution you as an operative can make towards the prevention of accidents is to work in the safest possible manner at all times, thus ensuring that your actions do not put at risk yourself, your workmates or the general public.

Safety: on site and in the workshop

A safe working area is a tidy working area. All unnecessary obstructions which may create a hazard should be removed, e.g. offcuts of material, unwanted materials, disused items of plant, and the extraction or flattening of nails from discarded pieces of timber. Therefore:

Clean up your workbench/work area periodically as offcuts and shavings are potential tripping and fire hazards.

Learn how to identify the different types of fire extinguishers and what type of fire they can safely be used on. Staff in each work area should be trained in the use of fire extinguishers, see **Table 4**.

Table 4 Use of fire extinguishers

USE OF FIRE EXTINGUISHERS						
	Red	Cream	Black	Blue	Green	Red
TYPE OF FIRE RISK	Water	Foam	Carbon dioxide	Dry powder	Vaporising liquid	Fire blanket
Paper, wood and textiles	✓	✓	✓	✓	✓	sed for smothering all types of fire
Flammable liquids and gases	✗	✓	✓	✓	✓	
Electrical hazard	✗	✗	✓	✓	✓	
Machinery and vehicles	✗	✗	✓	✓	✓	
	Suitable ✓			Unsuitable ✗		

WARNING!

FIRE EXTINGUISHERS CAN GIVE OFF DANGEROUS FUMES

Careful disposal of materials from heights is essential. They should always be lowered safely and not thrown or dropped from scaffolds and window openings etc. Even a small bolt or fitting dropped from a height can penetrate a person's skull and almost certainly lead to brain damage or death.

Ensure your tools are in good condition. Blunt cutting tools, loose hammer heads, broken or missing handles and mushroom heads must be repaired immediately or the use of the tool discontinued.

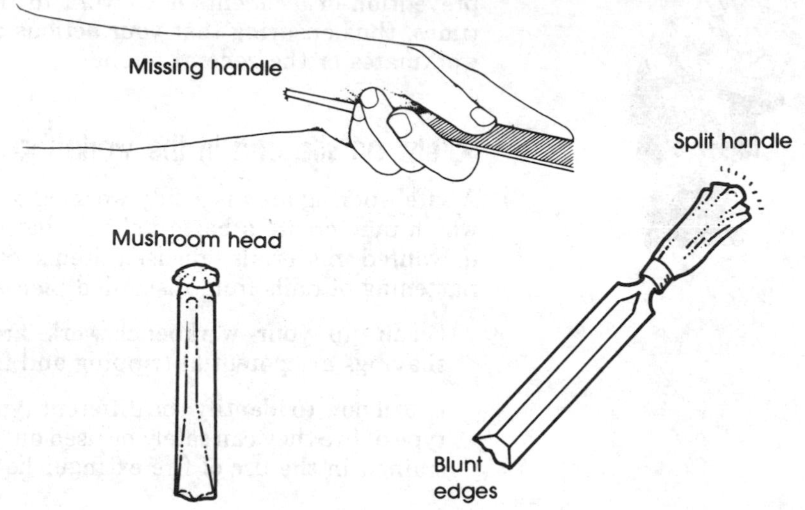

Unsafe tools

When moving materials and equipment always look at the job first; if it is too big for you then get help. Look out for splinters, nails, and sharp or jagged edges on the items to be moved. Always lift with your back straight, elbows tucked in, knees bent and feet slightly apart. When putting an item down ensure that your hands and fingers will not be trapped.

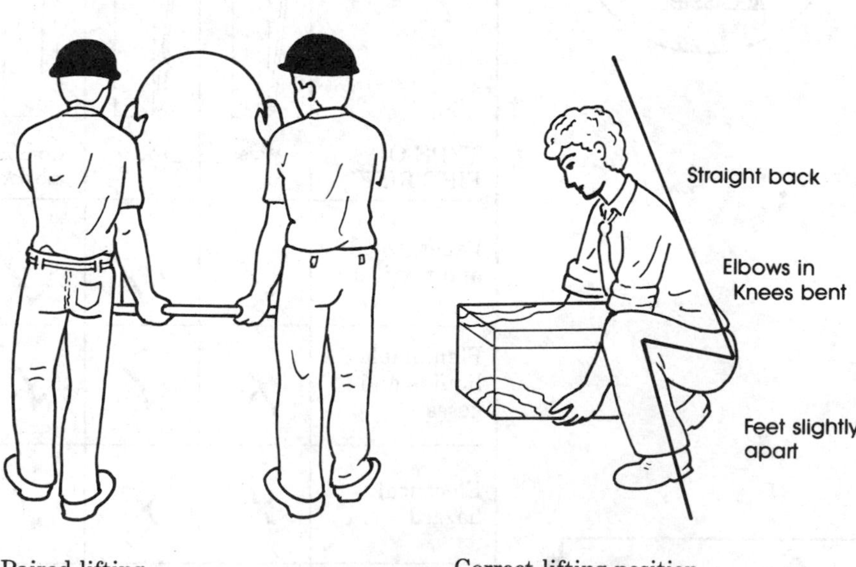

Paired lifting

Correct lifting position

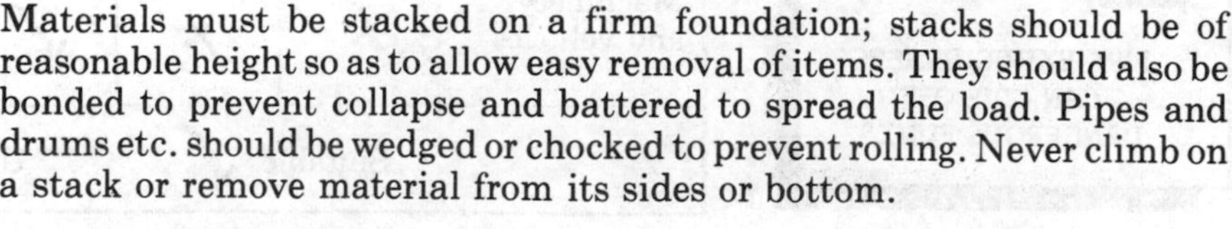

Materials must be stacked on a firm foundation; stacks should be of reasonable height so as to allow easy removal of items. They should also be bonded to prevent collapse and battered to spread the load. Pipes and drums etc. should be wedged or chocked to prevent rolling. Never climb on a stack or remove material from its sides or bottom.

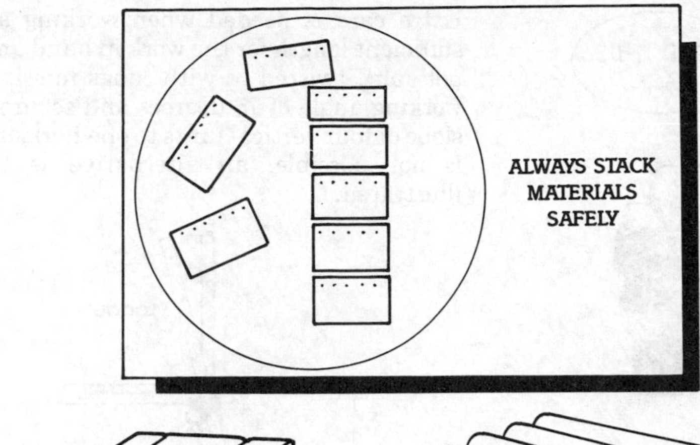

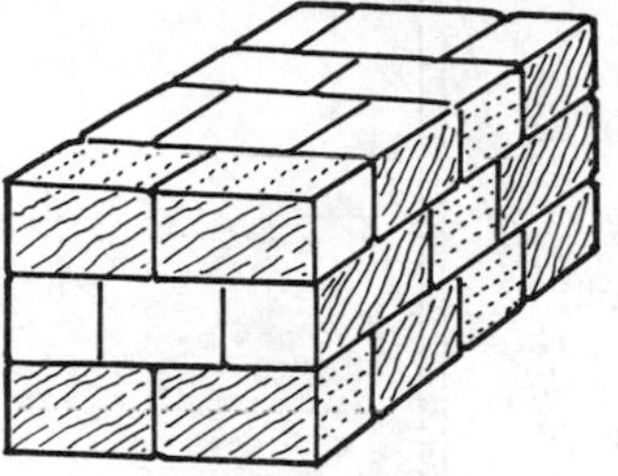

Bonded material storage

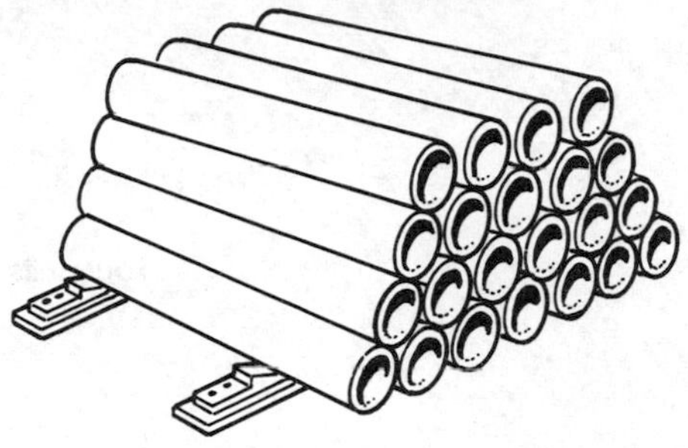

Chocked material storage

Excavations and inspection chambers should be either protected by a barrier or covered over completely to prevent people carelessly falling into them.

Protection of excavations

Extra care is needed when working at heights. Ladders should be of sufficient length for the work in hand and should be in good condition and not split, twisted or with rungs missing. They should also be used at a working angle of 75 degrees and securely tied at the top. This angle is a slope of four vertical units to one horizontal unit. Where a fixing at the top is not possible, an alternative is the stake-and-guy rope method illustrated.

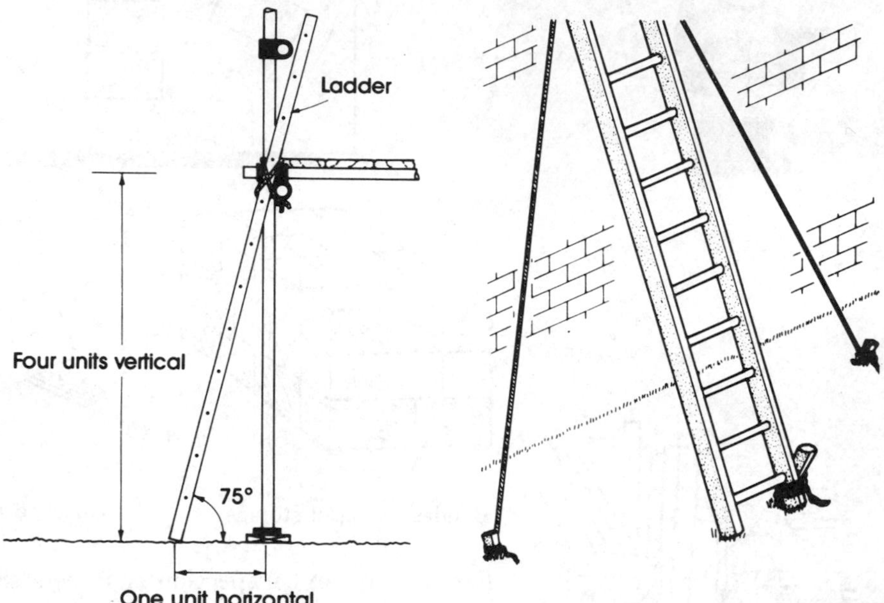

Ladder access Stakes and guys

Scaffolds should be inspected before working on them. Check to see that all components are there and in good condition, not bent, twisted, rusty, split, loose or out of plumb and level. Also ensure that the base has not been undermined or is too close to excavations. If in doubt do not use, and have it looked at by an experienced scaffolder. For further information see '*Scaffolding*' (page 105).

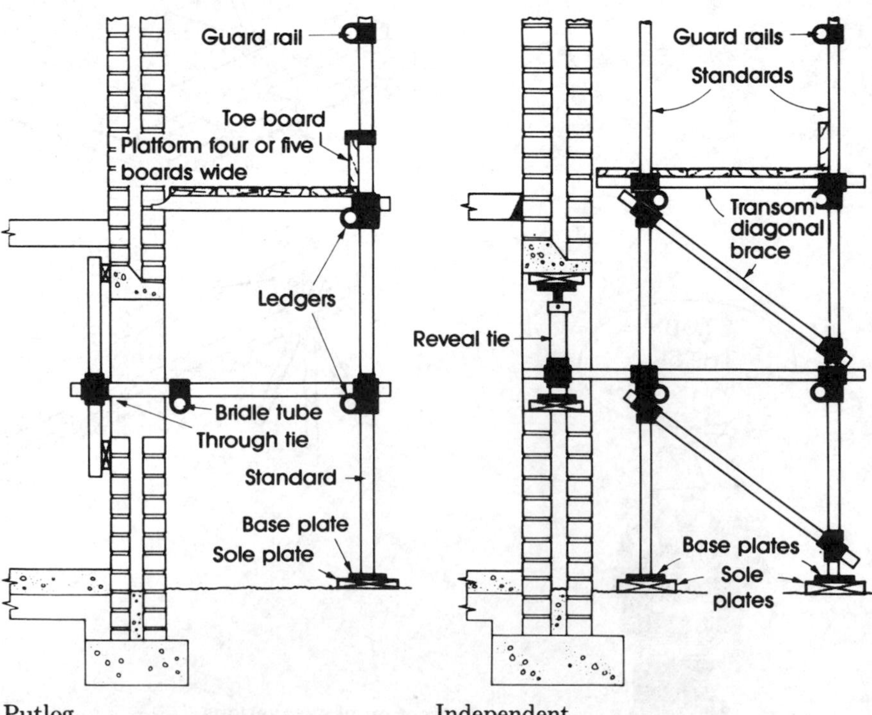

Putlog Independent

When working on roofs, roofing ladders or crawl boards should be used to provide safe access and/or to avoid falling through fragile coverings.

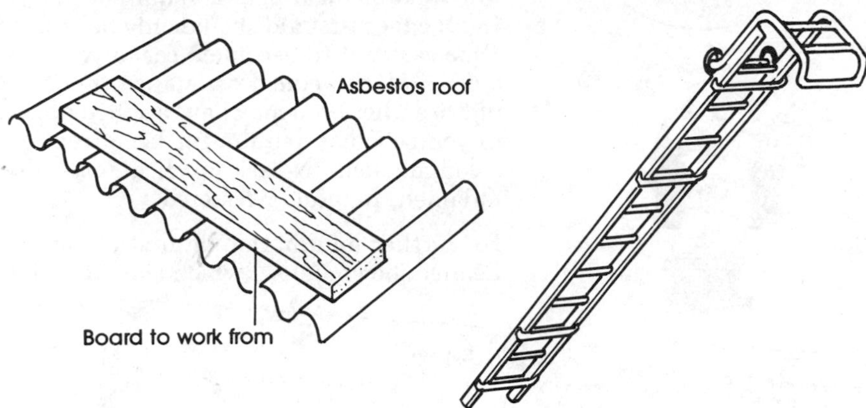

Crawl board

Roofing ladder

Working with electrical and compressed-air equipment brings additional hazards as they are both potential killers. Installations and equipment should be checked regularly by qualified personnel; if anything is incomplete, damaged, frayed, worn or loose, do not use it, but return it to stores for attention. Ensure cables and hoses are kept as short as possible and routed safely out of the way to prevent risk of tripping and damage, or in the case of electric cables, from lying in damp conditions.

Always wear the correct protective equipment for the work in hand. **Safety helmets** and **safety footwear** should be worn at all times. Wear **ear protectors** when carrying out noisy activities, and **safety goggles** when carrying out any operation that is likely to produce dust, chips or sparks, etc. **Dust masks** or **respirators** should be worn where dust is being produced or fumes are present, and **gloves** when handling materials. **Wet weather clothing** is necessary for inclement conditions. **Many of these items must be supplied free of charge by your employer**.

Care should be taken with personal hygiene which is just as important as physical protection. Some building materials have an irritant effect on contact with the skin. Some are poisonous if swallowed, while others can result in a state of unconsciousness (narcosis) if their vapour or powder is inhaled. These harmful effects can be avoided by taking proper precautions: follow the manufacturer's instructions; avoid inhaling fumes or powders; wear a barrier cream; thoroughly wash your hands before eating, smoking and after work.

First aid is the treatment of persons with the purpose of preserving life until medical help is obtained and also the treatment of minor injuries for which no medical help is required.

In all cases first aid should only be administered by a trained first-aider. Take care not to become a casualty yourself! Send for the nearest first-aider and/or medical assistance (phone 999) immediately. Even minor injuries where you may have applied a simple plaster or sterilised dressing to yourself may require further attention. **Remember** you are strongly recommended to seek medical attention if a minor injury becomes inflamed, painful or festered.

For further information on first aid see the General First Aid Guidance Leaflet shown below, which should be found in every first aid box.

Health and Safety (First Aid) Regulations 1981

General first aid guidance for first aid boxes

Note: Take care not to become a casualty yourself while administering first aid. Be sure to use protective clothing and equipment where necessary. If you are not a trained first-aider, send immediately for the nearest first-aider where one is available.

Advice on treatment

If the assistance of medical or nursing personnel will be required, send for a doctor or nurse (where they are employed at the workplace) or ambulance immediately. When an ambulance is called, arrangements should be made for it to be directed to the scene without delay.

Priorities

(1) *Breathing* If the casualty has stopped breathing, resuscitation must be started at once *before any other treatment is given* and should be continued until breathing is restored until medical, nursing or ambulance personnel take over.

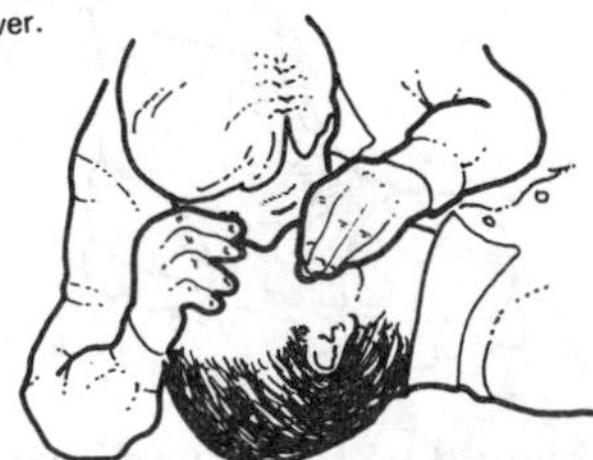

Mouth-to-mouth resuscitation

(2) *Bleeding* If bleeding is more than minimal, control it by direct pressure – apply a pad of sterilised dressing or, if necessary, direct pressure with fingers or thumb on the bleeding point. Raising a limb if the bleeding is sited there will help reduce the flow of blood (unless the limb is fractured).

(3) *Unconsciousness* Where the patient is unconscious, care must be taken to keep the airway open. This may be done by clearing the mouth and ensuring that the tongue does not block the back of the throat. Where possible, the casualty should be placed in the recovery position.

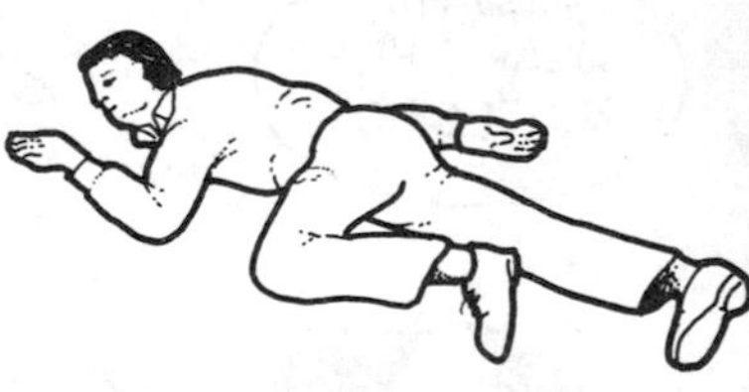

Recovery position

(4) *Broken bones* Unless the casualty is in a position which exposes him to further danger, do not attempt to move a casualty with suspected broken bones or injured joints until the injured parts have been supported. Secure so that the injured parts cannot move.

(5) *Other injuries*

(a) *Burns and scalds* Small burns and scalds should be treated by flushing the affected area with plenty of clean cool water before applying a sterilised dressing or a clean towel. Where the burn is large or deep, simply apply a dry sterile dressing. (N.B. Do not burst blisters or remove clothing sticking to the burns or scalds).

(b) *Chemical burns* Remove any contaminated clothing which shows no sign of sticking to the skin and flush all affected parts of the body with plenty of clean, cool water ensuring that all the chemical is so diluted as to be rendered harmless. Apply a sterilised dressing to exposed, damaged skin and clean towels to damaged areas where the clothing cannot be removed. (N.B. Take care when treating the casualty to avoid contamination).

(c) *Foreign bodies in the eye* If the object cannot be removed readily with a clean piece of moist material, irrigate with clean, cool water. People with eye injuries which are more than minimal must be sent to hospital with the eye covered with an eye pad from the container.

(d) *Chemical in the eye* Flush the open eye at once with clean, cool water; continue for at least 5 to 10 minutes and, in any case of doubt, even longer. If the contamination is more than minimal, send the casualty to hospital.

(e) *Electric shock* Ensure that the current is switched off. If this is impossible, free the person, using heavy duty insulating gloves (to BS 697/1977) where these are provided for this purpose near the first aid container, or using something made of rubber, dry cloth or wood or a folded newspaper; use the casualty's own clothing if dry. *Be careful* not to touch the casualty's skin before the current is switched off. If breathing is failing or has stopped, start resuscitation and continue until breathing is restored or medical, nursing or ambulance personnel take over.

(f) *Gassing* Move the casualty to fresh air *but make sure that whoever does this is wearing suitable respiratory protection.* If breathing has stopped, start resuscitation and continue until breathing is restored or until medical, nursing or ambulance personnel take over. If the casualty needs to go to hospital make sure a note of the gas involved is sent with him.

General

(a) *Hygiene* When possible, wash your hands before treating wounds, burns or eye injuries. Take care in any event not to contaminate the surfaces of dressings

(b) *Treatment position* Casualties should be seated or lying down while being treated

(c) *Record-keeping* An entry must be made in the accident book (for example B1 510 Social Security Act Book) of each case

(d) *Minor injuries* Casualties with minor injuries, of a sort they would attend to themselves if at home, may wash their hands and apply a small sterilised dressing from the container

(e) *First aid materials* Each article used from the container should be replaced as soon as possible

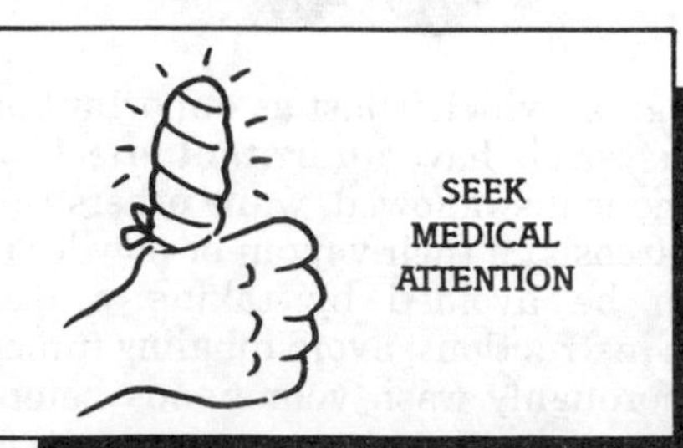

SEEK MEDICAL ATTENTION

Questions for you

10. The correct angle for an access ladder to a scaffold is:
(a) 1 unit horizontal, 2 units vertical
(b) 1 unit horizontal, 4 units vertical
(c) 2 units horizontal, 1 unit vertical
(d) 4 units horizontal, 1 unit vertical

a	b	c	d

11. State **FOUR** building site operations where you would insist on the use of protective equipment. Name the item of protective equipment in each case.

12. Describe **FOUR** general procedures to be followed, which would aid either site or workshop safety.

Hazard spotting

The following exercise is intended to reinforce the work undertaken in this package. It gives you an opportunity to use your newly acquired safety awareness.

From the illustration (pages 64–5) of an unsafe building site, you are required to identify safety hazards, breaches of regulations and general bad practices, etc.

There are at least 20 to be found, which relate to areas covered as part of this package.

How many hazards can you spot?

Circle each hazard etc. and number it like this:

Then describe each hazard etc. like this:

(1) Sole plate missing from under scaffold standard.

Hazards spotted

(1) ______________________________

(2) ______________________________

(3) ______________________________

(4) ______________________________

(5) ______________________________

(6) ______________________________

(7) ______________________________

(8) ______________________________

(9) ______________________________

(10) ______________________________

(11) ______________________________

(12) ______________________________

(13) ______________________________

(14) ______________________________

(15) ______________________________

(16) ______________________________

(17) ______________________________

(18) ______________________________

(19) ______________________________

(20) ______________________________

(21) ______________________________

(22) ______________________________

(23) ______________________________

(24) ______________________________

(25) ______________________________

BBS
ON HIRE

SPOT THE HAZARDS
NO WAY WOULD I WORK HERE
THINK SAFETY DON'T BECOME A STATISTIC
NTRACT

WORD-SQUARE SEARCH

Hidden in the word square are 14 words associated with safety. You may find the words written forwards, backwards, up, down and diagonally. Solve the clues and then see if you can find the words.

CLUES

This package has raised your _______ awareness.
Used at a working angle of 75 degrees. _______
Safety ________ should be worn at all times.
An event causing injury or damage. __________
A notice to stop work immediately. ______________
Carried out before eating. _____
Statutory legislation (abbreviation). ________
Should be covered. ____________
About 140 each year are ______.
A HSE inspector may _____ premises to carry out investigations.
Notifiable dangerous occurrences must be __________ to the HSE.
Scaffolding is covered under the ______________ regulations.

Draw a ring around the words, or line in using a highlight pen thus:

EXAMPLE

EXAMPLE

A	C	R	I	B	Z	F	A	L	B	A	D	P	E	T	E	R	E
C	H	R	I	S	I	H	S	A	L	E	B	R	E	T	T	E	F
C	R	L	S	L	L	A	F	D	A	D	E	O	R	I	P	P	G
S	I	C	A	V	T	S	A	D	L	P	P	H	I	V	E	O	H
D	A	D	D	A	Y	A	T	A	P	O	C	I	E	B	H	R	A
B	U	I	L	N	T	W	T	R	R	T	C	B	I	L	E	T	T
C	R	E	T	N	E	A	L	E	O	T	D	I	A	W	L	E	E
Q	T	W	V	J	F	G	D	A	B	L	F	T	H	A	M	D	S
T	A	T	E	F	A	S	Y	D	I	E	O	I	T	R	E	B	E
W	C	C	O	N	S	T	R	U	C	T	I	O	N	V	T	C	W
X	C	O	B	C	A	C	O	N	S	T	G	N	I	H	S	A	W
U	B	N	E	F	S	R	T	R	S	L	A	F	A	V	T	I	N
R	Q	S	P	V	R	D	A	C	C	I	D	E	N	T	P	E	R
O	E	T	V	N	N	P	D	C	A	N	E	D	I	C	C	A	C
L	A	R	D	E	R	B	N	H	I	B	I	T	T	I	L	N	A
C	A	U	T	I	O	L	A	D	D	E	R	S	O	D	O	D	V
F	A	C	T	A	L	B	M	L	A	D	E	D	E	R	S	I	E
C	S	N	O	I	T	A	V	A	C	X	E	C	I	D	E	N	T

3 Communications

Scale

A scale rule has a series of marks used for measuring purposes.

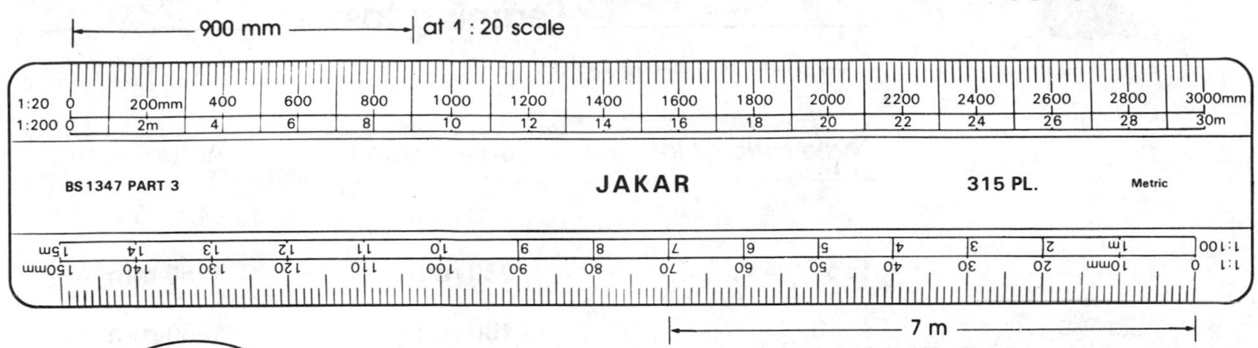

READ THIS PAGE

Scales use ratios to relate measurements on a drawing or model to the real dimensions of the actual job. It is impractical to draw buildings, plots of land and most parts of a building to their full size, as they simply will not fit on a piece of paper.

Instead they are normally drawn to a smaller size which has a known ratio to the real thing. These are then called scale drawings.

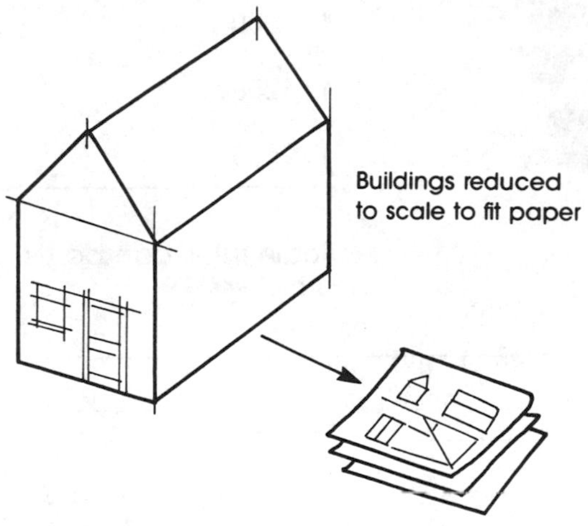

IT'S DRAWN SMALLER THAN IT REALLY IS

The main scales used in the construction industry are:
1 : 1 1 : 5 1 : 10 1 : 20 1 : 50 1 : 100 1 : 200 1 : 500 1 : 1250 1 : 2500

The ratio shows how many times bigger one quantity is than the other. In a house drawing to a scale of 1 : 20, 1 mm on the drawing would stand for 20 mm in the actual house; if the drawing was to a scale of 1 : 100, 1 mm would stand for 100 mm and so on.

An object drawn 100 mm long would represent a much bigger size.

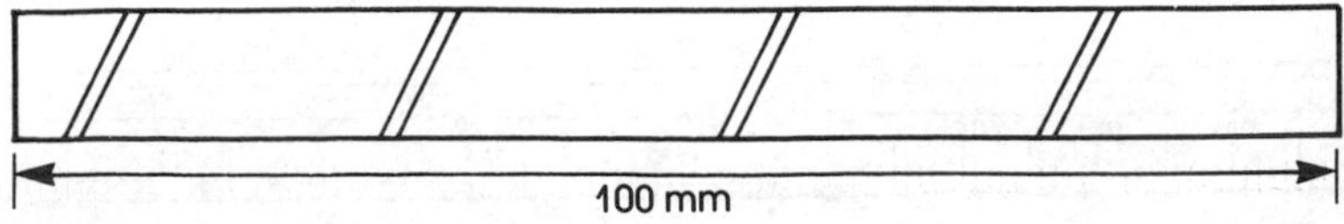

To a scale of 1 : 10 it would represent 1000 mm or 1 m. Whereas to a scale of 1 : 50 it would represent 5000 mm or 5 m.

It is simply a matter of multiplying the scale measurement by the scale ratio:

Example
10 mm at a 1 : 50 scale equals 500 mm

Learning task

Complete the table below.

Scale ratio of job	*Size drawn*	*Actual size*
1 : 1	100 mm	100 mm
1 : 5	250 mm	1250 mm
1 : 10	100 mm	1000 mm
1 : 20	75 mm	
1 : 50	125 mm	
1 : 100	150 mm	
1 : 200	125 mm	
1 : 1500	45 mm	
1 : 1250	25 mm	
1 : 2500	50 mm	

Scale rules can be used for both preparing and reading scale drawings.

1:1 0 10mm 20 30 40 50 60 70 80 90 100 110 120 130 140 150mm
1:100 1m 2 3 4 5 6 7 8 9 10 11 12 13 14 15m

1:20 0 200mm 400 600 800 1000 1200 1400 1600 1800 2000 2200 2400 2600 2800 3000mm
1:200 0 2m 4 6 8 10 12 14 16 18 20 22 24 26 28 30m

BS 1347 PART 3 JAKAR 315 PL. Metric

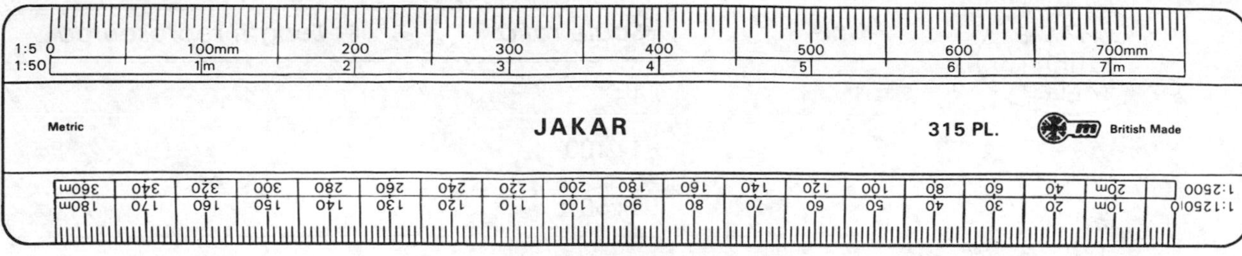

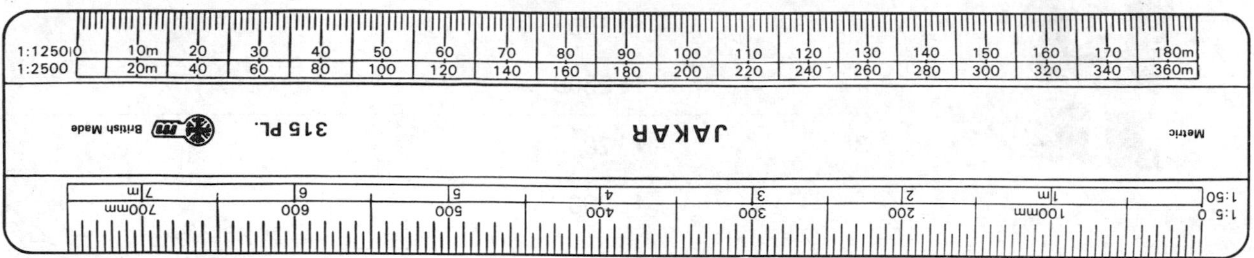

Select a scale rule and mark on it lines representing:

7 m to a scale of 1 : 50

1200 mm to a scale of 1 : 100

600 mm to a scale of 1 : 200

85 m to a scale of 1 : 1250.

Use a scale rule to measure the following lines and then complete the table.

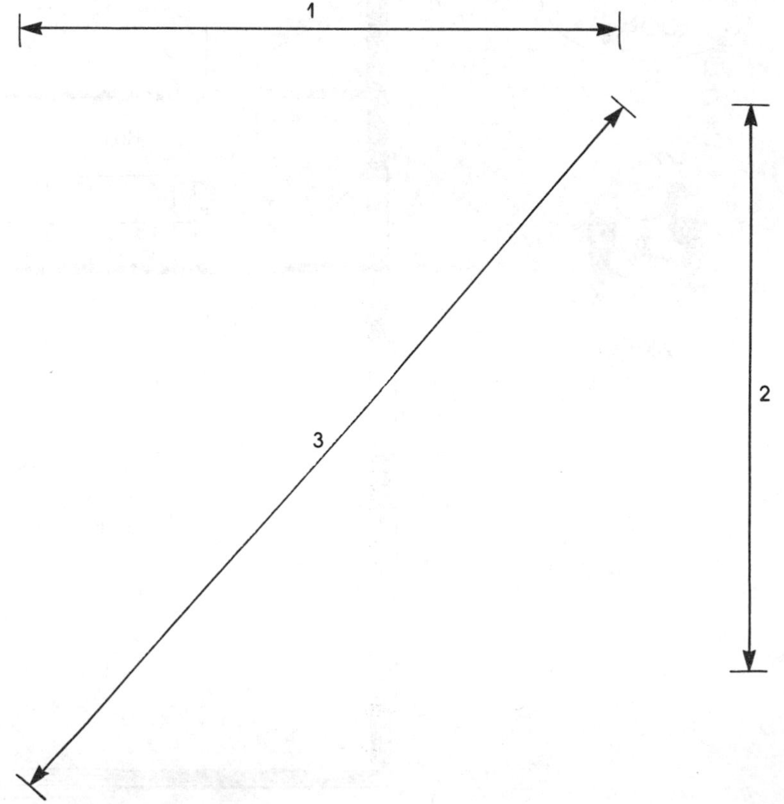

Line	*Scale ratio*	*Length represented*
1	1 : 1	
	1 : 100	
	1 : 50	
2	1 : 5	
	1 : 100	
	1 : 2500	
3	1 : 20	
	1 : 200	
	1 : 1250	

The outline ground floor plan of a house is drawn to a scale of 1 : 50.

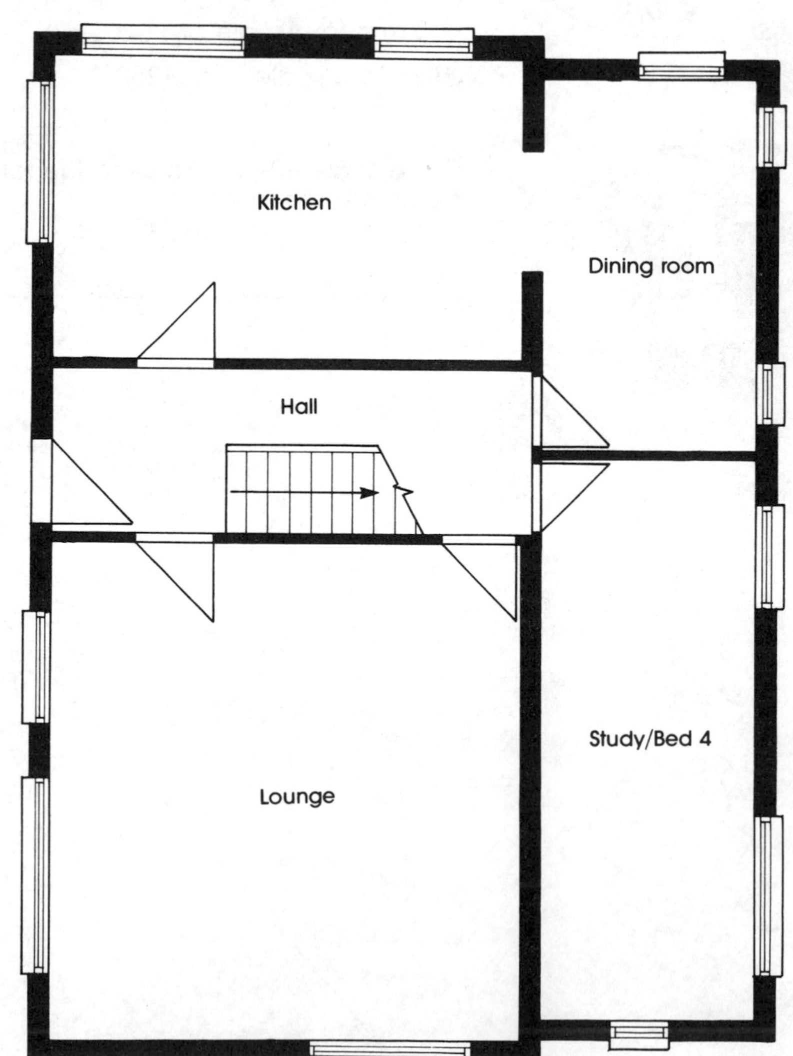

Use your scale rule to fill in the table.

Room	*Length*	*Width*	*Length of skirting*
Lounge			
Dining room			
Kitchen			
Study/Bed 4			
Hall			

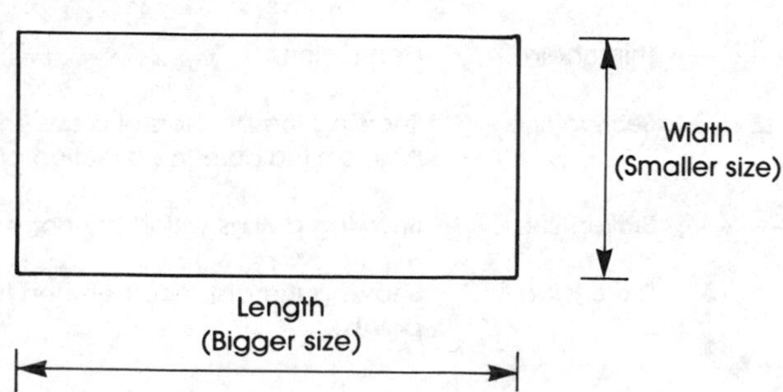

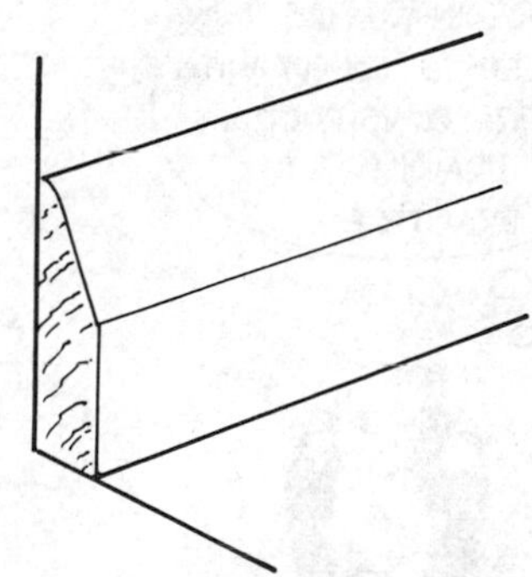

Skirting is the piece of wood fixed at the junction of the floor and wall joint

Drawings, symbols and abbreviations

Drawings

These are the major means used to communicate technical information between all parties involved in the building process. They must be clear, accurate and easily understood by everyone who uses them. In order to achieve this architects and designers will use standardised methods for layout, symbols and abbreviations.

Line	Use
Thick	Main outlines
Medium	General details and outlines
Thin	Construction and dimension lines
Breakline	Breaks in the continuity of a drawing
Thick chain	Pipe lines, drains and services
Thin chain	Centre lines
Section line	Showing the position of a cut (the pointers indicate the direction of view)
Broken line	Showing details which are not visible
Dimension line	Showing the distance between two points

Symbols

These are graphical illustrations used to represent different materials and components in a building drawing.

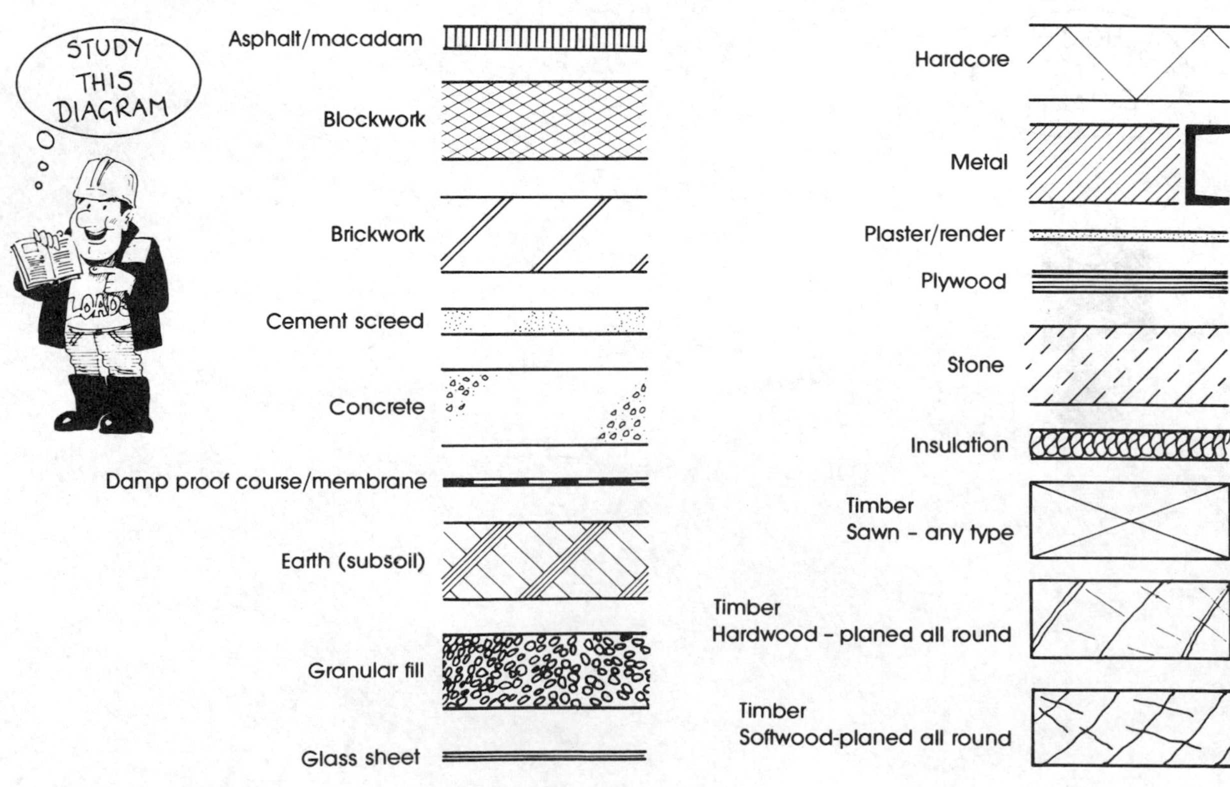

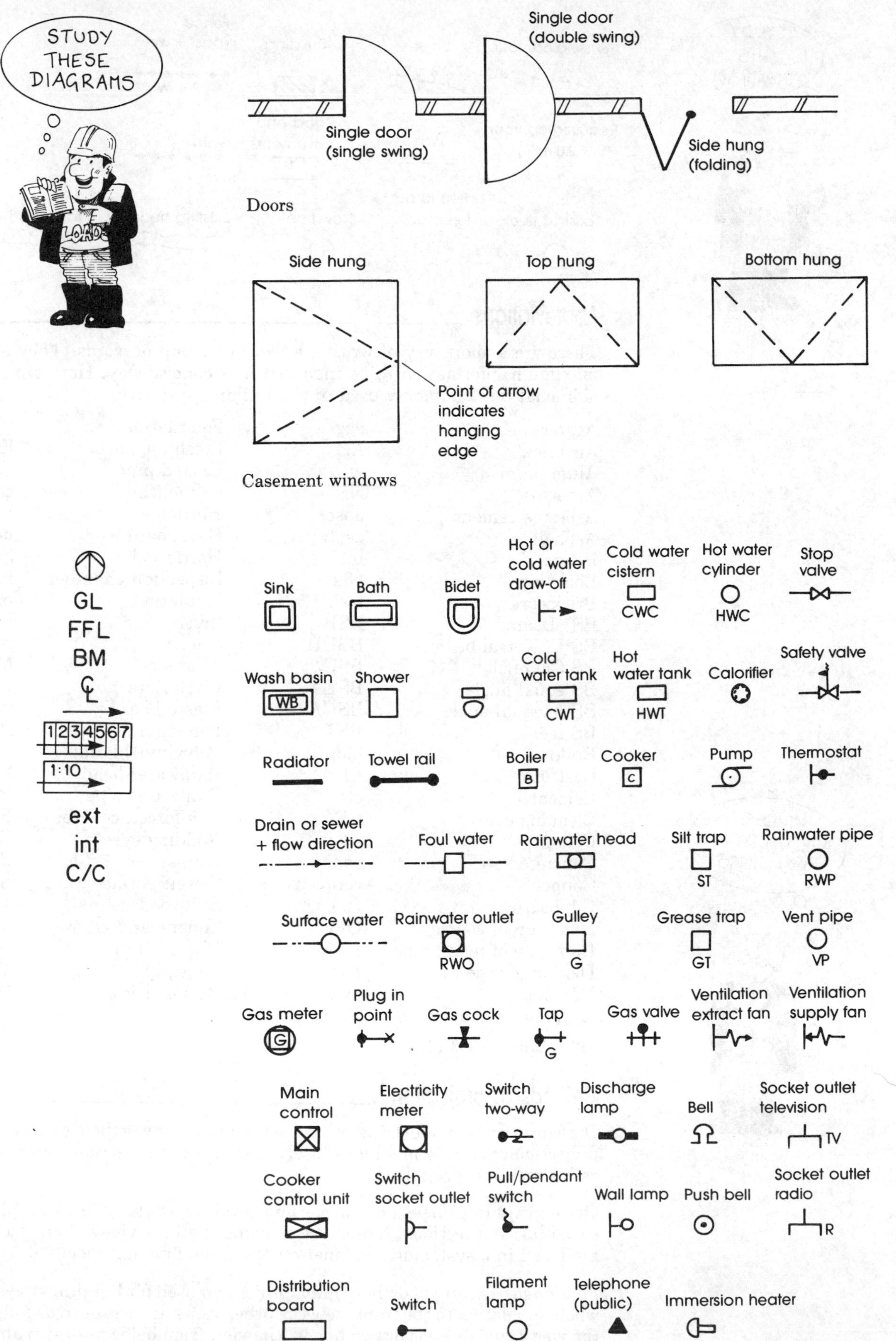
STUDY THESE DIAGRAMS
LOADS
Single door (double swing)
Single door (single swing)
Side hung (folding)
Doors
Side hung
Top hung
Bottom hung
Point of arrow indicates hanging edge
Casement windows
GL
FFL
BM
C
L
1234567
1:10
ext
int
C/C
Sink
Bath
Bidet
Hot or cold water draw-off
Cold water cistern
CWC
Hot water cylinder
HWC
Stop valve
Wash basin
WB
Shower
Cold water tank
CWT
Hot water tank
HWT
Calorifier
Safety valve
Radiator
Towel rail
Boiler
B
Cooker
C
Pump
Thermostat
Drain or sewer + flow direction
Foul water
Rainwater head
Silt trap
ST
Rainwater pipe
RWP
Surface water
Rainwater outlet
RWO
Gulley
G
Grease trap
GT
Vent pipe
VP
Gas meter
G
Plug in point
Gas cock
Tap
G
Gas valve
Ventilation extract fan
Ventilation supply fan
Main control
Electricity meter
Switch two-way
2
Discharge lamp
Bell
Socket outlet television
TV
Cooker control unit
Switch socket outlet
Pull/pendant switch
Wall lamp
Push bell
Socket outlet radio
R
Distribution board
Switch
Filament lamp
Telephone (public)
Immersion heater

Existing contour 5.0 m

Bank

Building

Fence (post + wire)

P + W

Required contour 2.0 m

Wall

Road and pavement

Gate

Existing tree

Tree to be removed

New tree

Existing hedge

Proposed hedge

Abbreviations

These are a short way of writing a word or group of words. They allow maximum information to be included in a concise way. Here are some abbreviations commonly used in the building industry.

Aggregate	agg	Foundation	fdn
Air brick	AB	Fresh air inlet	FAI
Aluminium	al	Glazed pipe	GP
Asbestos	abs	Granolithic	grano
Asbestos cement	absct	Hardcore	hc
Asphalt	asph	Hardboard	hdbd
Bitumen	bit	Hardwood	hwd
Boarding	bdg	Inspection chamber	IC
Brickwork	bwk	Insulation	insul
BS* Beam	BSB	Invert	inv
BS Universal beam	BSUB	Joist	jst
BS Channel	BSC	Mild steel	MS
BS equal angle	BSEA	Pitch fibre	PF
BS unequal angle	BSUA	Plasterboard	pbd
BS tee	BST	Polyvinyl acetate	PVA
Building	bldg	Polyvinylchloride	PVC
Cast iron	CI	Rainwater head	RWH
Cement	ct	Rainwater pipe	RWP
Cleaning eye	CE	Reinforced concrete	RC
Column	col	Rodding eye	RE
Concrete	conc	Foul sewers	FS
Copper	copp cu	Sewers surface water	SWS
Cupboard	cpd	Softwood	swd
Damp proof course	DPC	Tongue and groove	T&G
Damp proof membrane	DPM	Unglazed pipe	UGP
Discharge pipe	DP	Vent pipe	VP
Drawing	dwg	Wrought iron	WI
Expanded metal lathing	EML		

*BS = British Standard

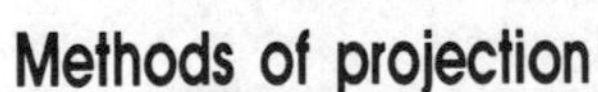

Methods of projection

Drawings can be produced as either a series of flat views called orthographic projection or in a form which closely resembles their actual appearance called pictorial projection.

Orthographic projection – a method used for working drawing plans, elevations and sections. A separate drawing of all the views of an object is produced in a systematic manner on the same drawing sheet.

First angle – a form of orthographic projection used for building drawings where in relation to the front view the other views are arranged as follows: the view from above is drawn below; the view from below is drawn above;

the view from the left is drawn to the right; the view from the right is drawn to the left; the view from the rear is drawn to the extreme right. A sectional view may be drawn to the left or the right.

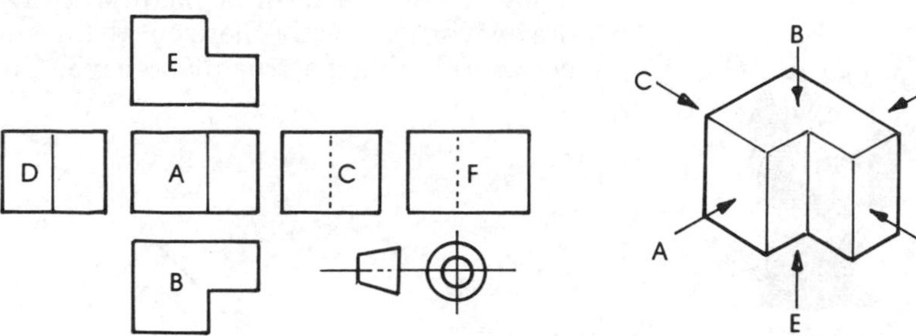

First angle

Isometric view

Third angle – a form of orthographic projection used for engineering drawings. It is also termed American projection. In relation to the front elevation the other views are arranged as follows: the view from above is drawn above; the view from below is drawn below; the view from the left is drawn left; the view from the right is drawn right; the view from the rear is drawn to the extreme right. A sectional view may be drawn to the left or the right.

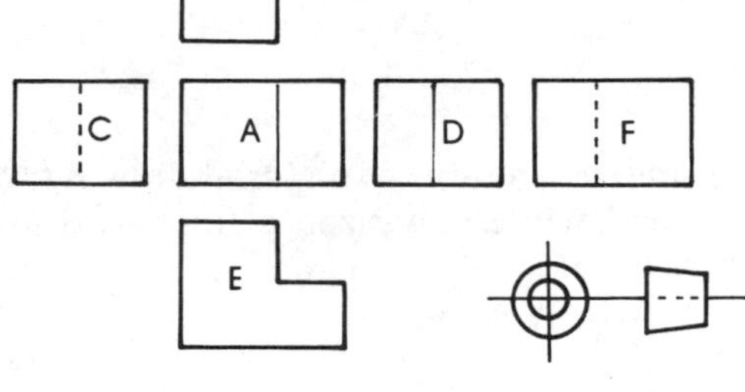

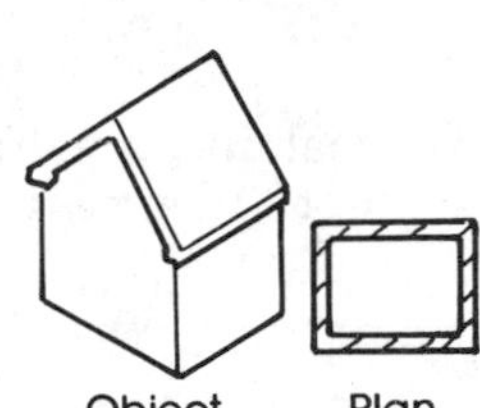

Third angle

Isometric view

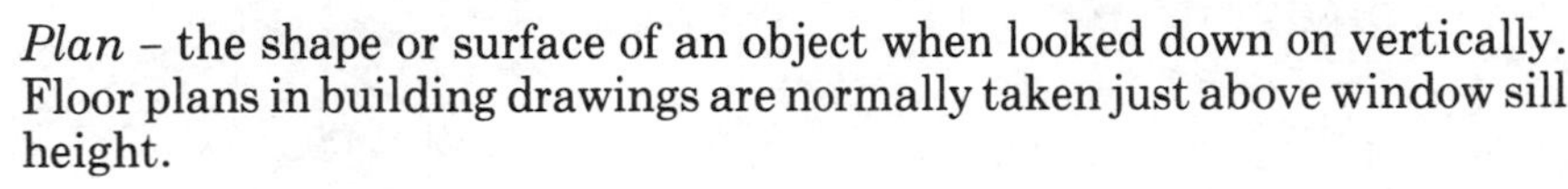

Plan – the shape or surface of an object when looked down on vertically. Floor plans in building drawings are normally taken just above window sill height.

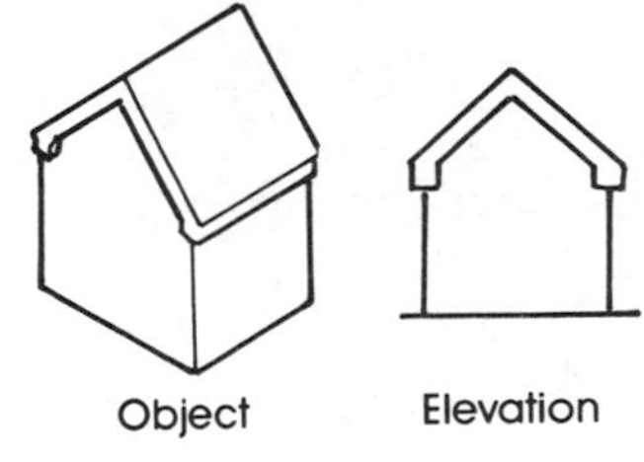

Elevation – the view of an object from either side, front or rear.

Section – the cut surface produced when an object is imaginarily cut through with a saw.

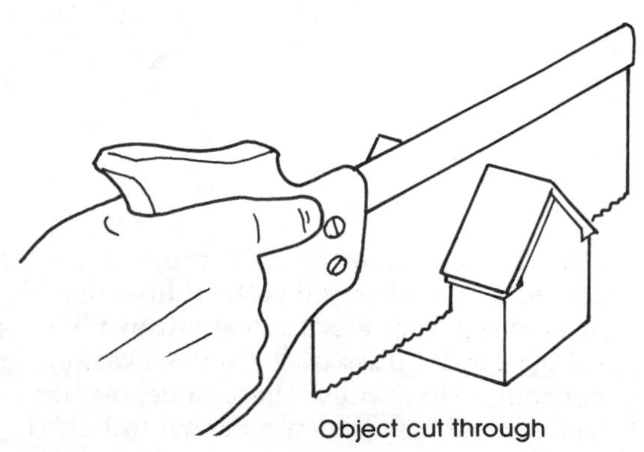

Object cut through

Section

Pictorial projection – a method of drawing objects in a three-dimensional form. Often used for design and marketing purposes, as the finished appearance of the object can be more readily appreciated.

Axonometric – a form of pictorial drawing where all vertical lines are drawn vertical, while horizontal lines are drawn at 45 degrees to the horizontal, giving a true plan shape. Often used in kitchen design.

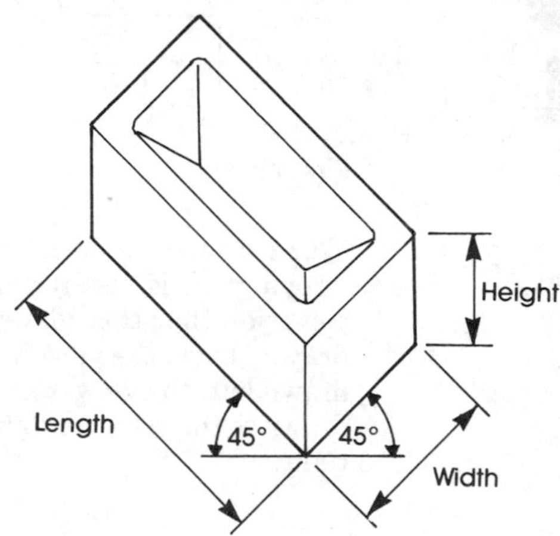

Isometric – a form of pictorial drawing where all vertical lines are drawn vertical, while all horizontal lines are drawn at an angle of 30 degrees to the horizontal.

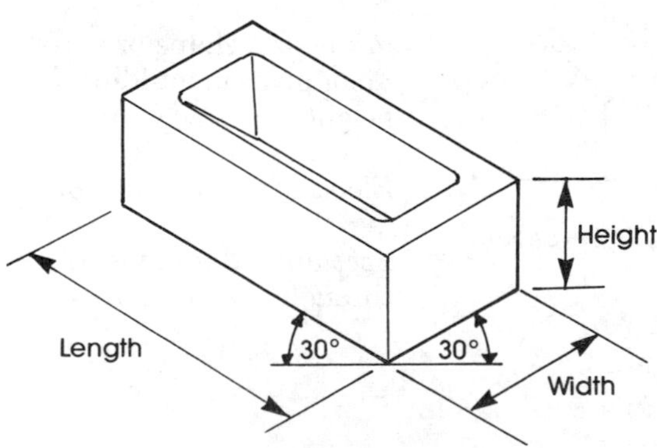

Oblique – a form of pictorial projection which can take the form of either cabinet or cavalier. All vertical lines are drawn vertical and all horizontal lines in the front elevation are drawn horizontal to give a true front view. All horizontal lines in the side elevations are drawn at 45 degrees to the horizontal. In cavalier these 45 degree lines are drawn to their full length, while in cabinet they are drawn to half their full length.

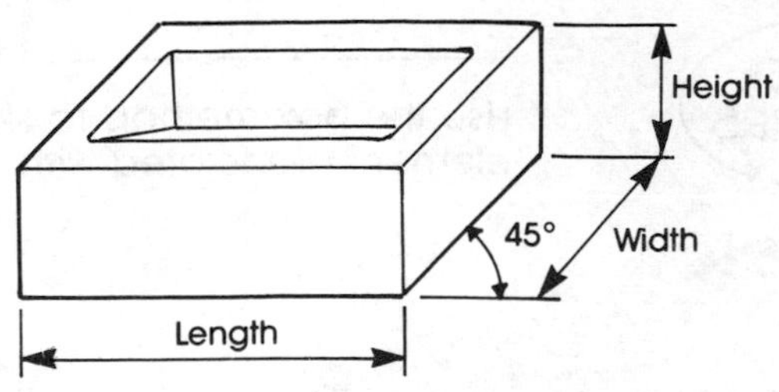

Cavalier

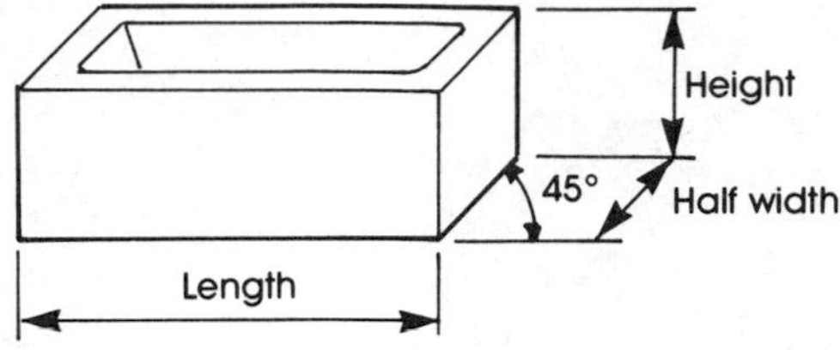

Cabinet

Sketches

These are rough outlines or initial drafts of an idea before full working drawings are made. Alternatively sketches may be prepared to convey thoughts and ideas. It is often much easier to produce a sketch of your intentions rather than to describe in words or produce a long list of instructions. Sketches can be produced either freehand, that is without the use of any equipment, or be more accurately produced using a ruler and set squares to give basic guidelines. Methods of projection follow those used for drawing, e.g. orthographic or pictorial.

Pictorial sketching is made easy if you imagine the object you wish to sketch with a three-dimensional box around it. Draw the box first, lightly, with a 2H pencil, then draw in the object using an HB pencil.

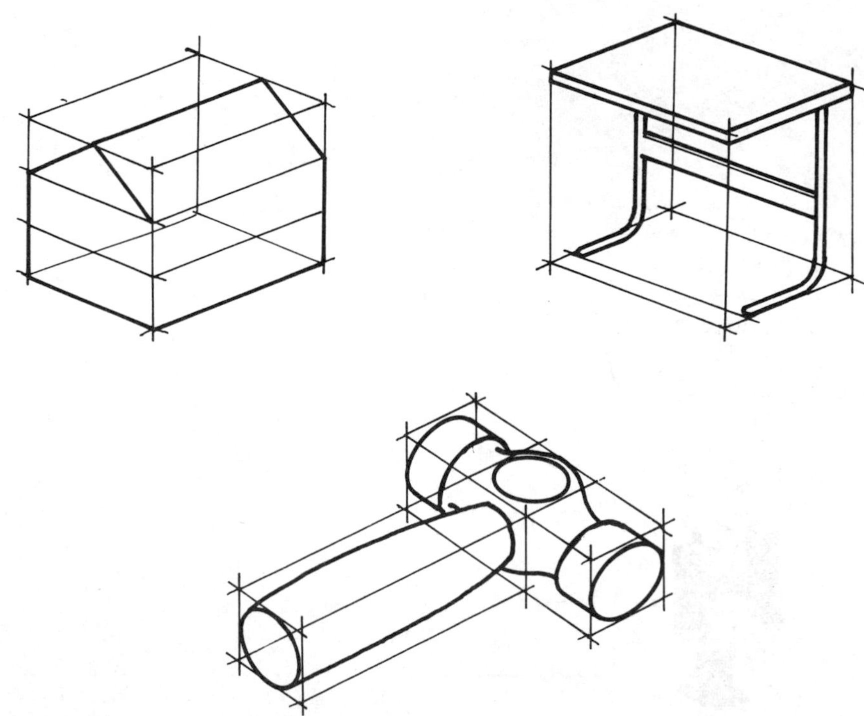

Learning task

Use the box method to sketch a hand tool and a component or element associated with your occupation.

Construction activity documents

Architects' drawings

A range of scale working drawings showing plans, elevations, general arrangements, layouts and details of a proposed construction, the main types being:

Location drawings

Block plans identify the proposed site in relation to the surrounding area.

The scales most commonly used are 1 : 2500 and 1 : 1250.

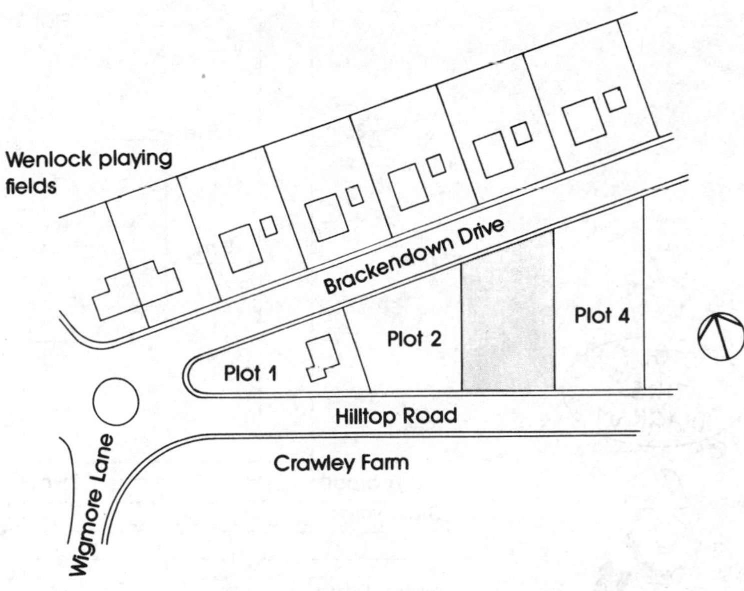

Site plans show the position of a proposed building and the general layout of the road services and drainage etc. on the site. The scales most commonly used are 1 : 500 and 1 : 200.

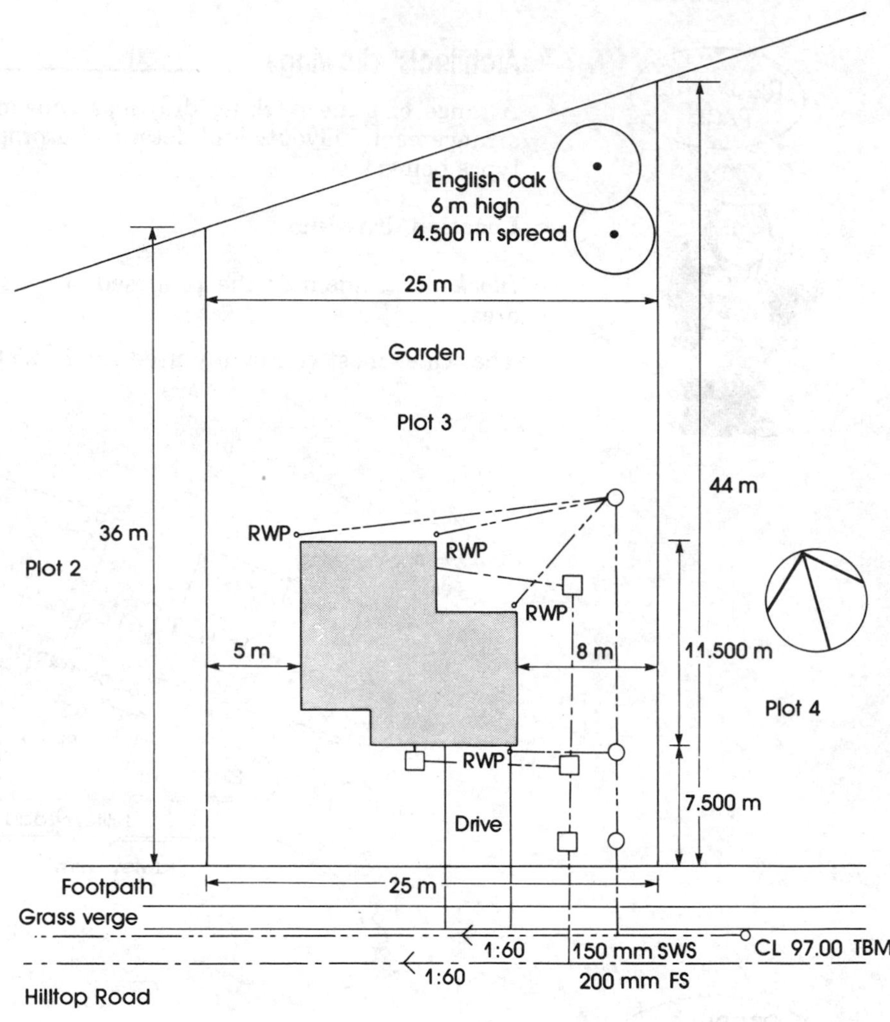

Site plan

General location plans show the positions occupied by the various areas within a building and identify the locations of principal elements and components. The scales most commonly used are 1 : 200, 1 : 100 and 1 : 50.

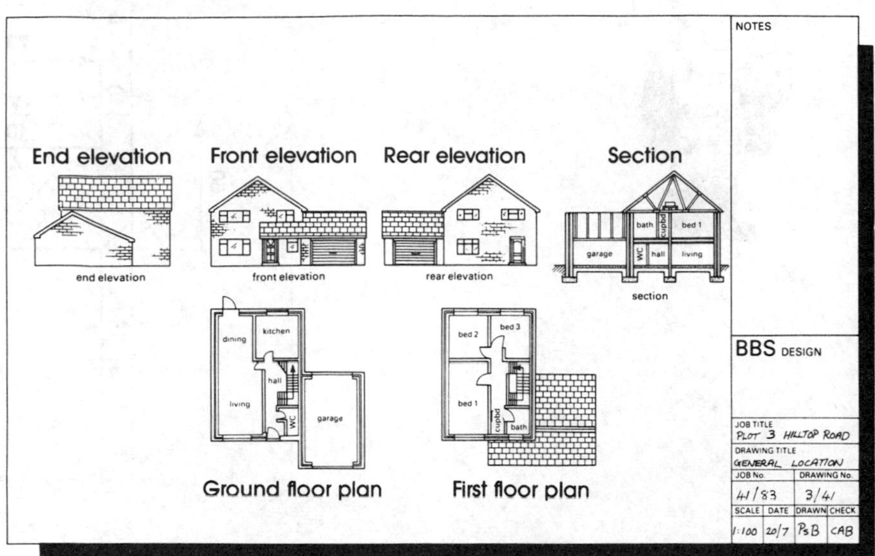

Component drawings

Range drawings show the basic sizes in a reference system of a standard range of building components. The scales most commonly used are 1 : 100, 1 : 50 and 1 : 20.

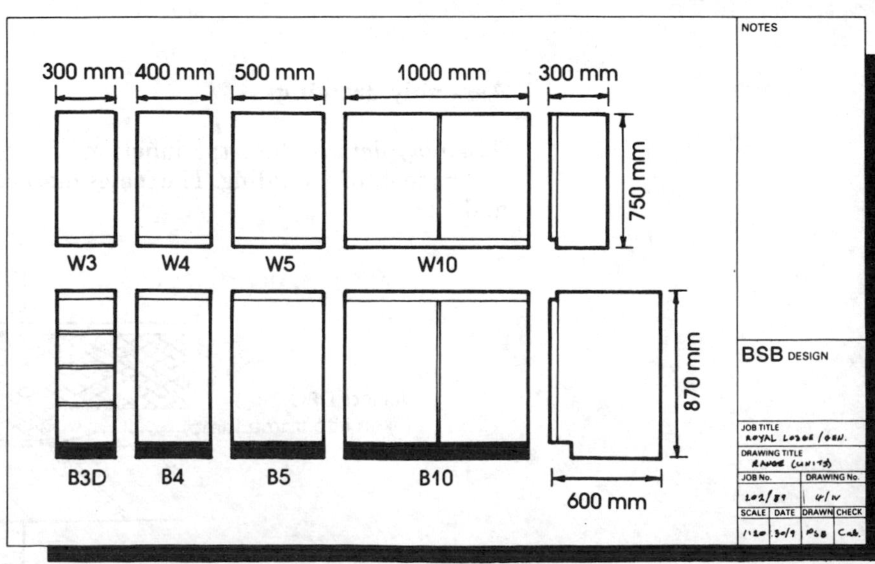

Detail drawings show all the information that is required to manufacture a particular component. The scales most commonly used are 1 : 10, 1 : 5 and 1 : 1.

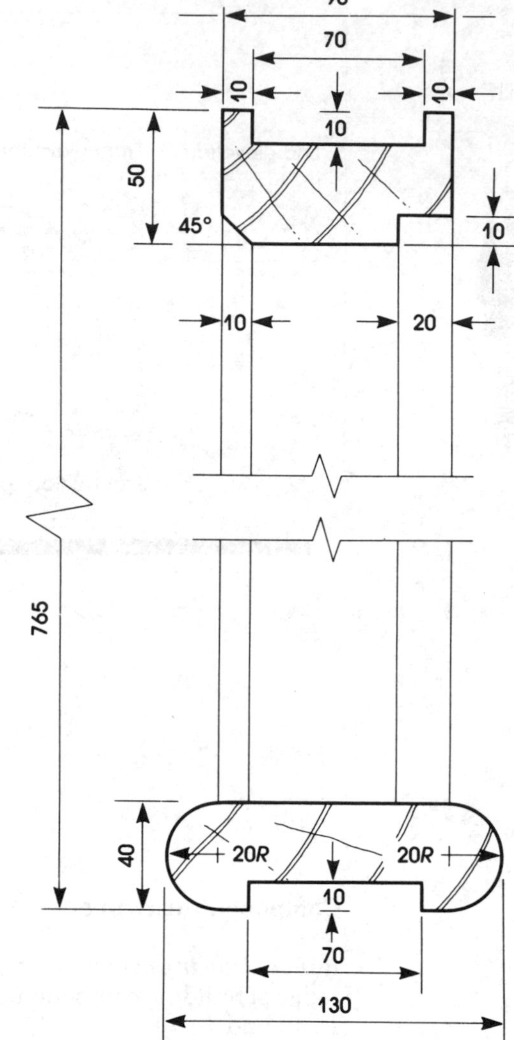

Assembly drawings

Assembly details show the junctions between the various elements and components of a building. The scales most commonly used are 1 : 20, 1 : 10 and 1 : 5.

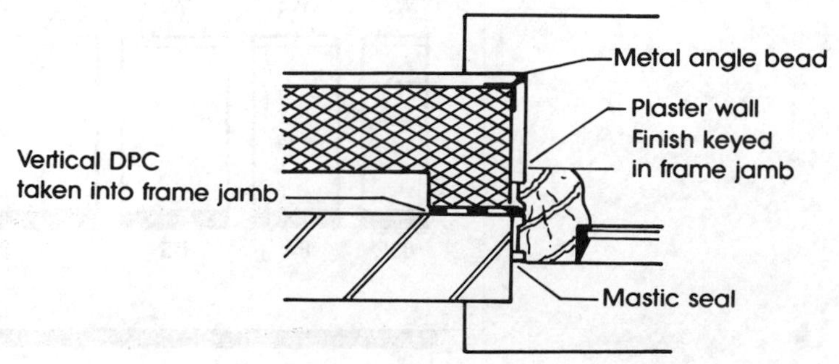

Dimensions are shown on drawings against a lightly drawn line with arrowheads terminating against short cross lines. Actual sizes may be shown individually as separate dimensions or cumulatively along a building as in running dimensions. Running dimensions are to be preferred for setting out rather than separate dimensions, since any inaccuracies or error made in marking one separate dimension will have a cumulative effect, throwing each successive position out. Where running dimensions are not shown on a drawing it is best to work them out and indicate against each position. As a check the total of the separate dimensions should equal the final position figure.

To avoid confusing the position of the decimal point, an oblique stroke is often used to separate metres and millimetres. Where the dimension is less than a metre a nought is inserted before the stroke.

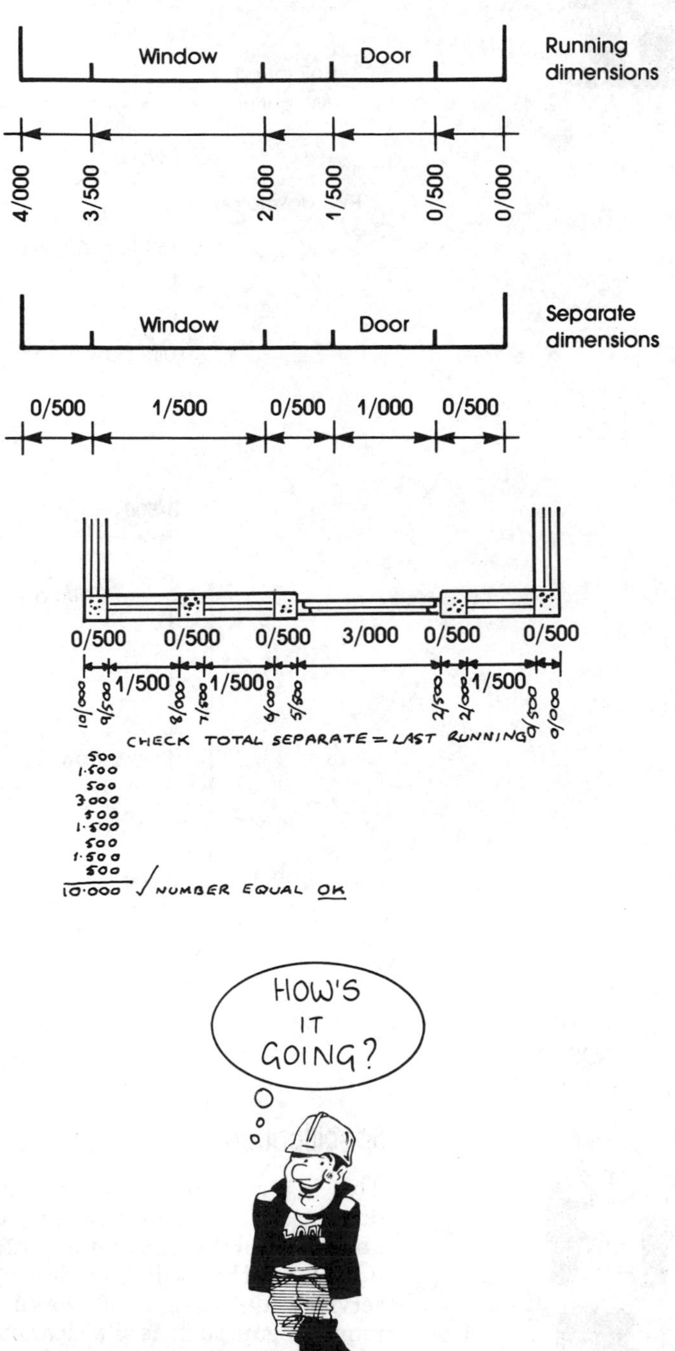

Learning task

Mark up the outline plan to show running dimensions including the check.

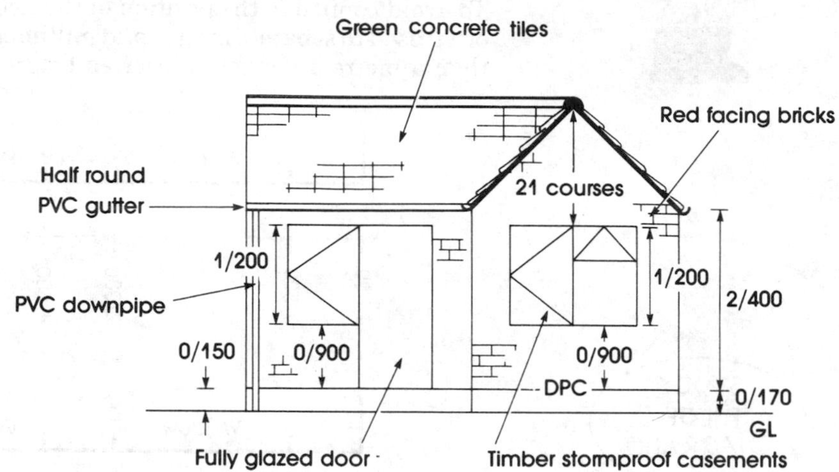

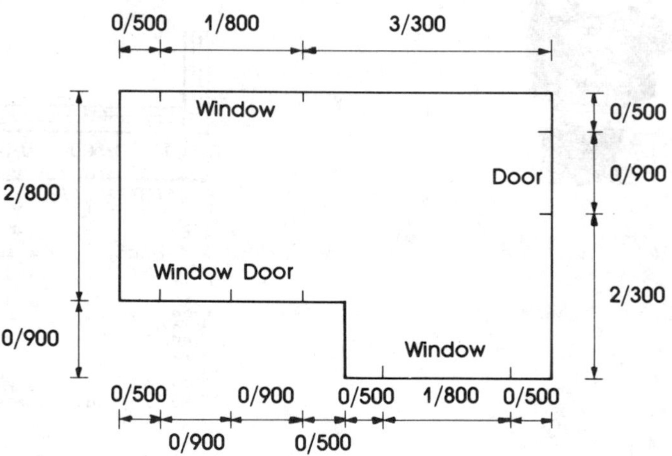

Specification

This is a contract document that supplements the architect's working drawings. It contains precise descriptions of all the essential information and job requirements that will affect the price, but cannot be shown on the drawings. This will include any site restrictions, availability of site services, description of workmanship and materials and any other requirements such as site clearance, making good on completion and who is responsible for approving finished work etc.

BBS DESIGN

Specification of the works to be carried out and the materials to be used in the erection and completion of a new house and garage on plot 3, Hilltop Road, Brackendowns, Bedfordshire, for Mr W. Whiteman, to the satisfaction of the architect.

1.00 General conditions

1.01
1.02

1.03
1.04

2.00
2.01
2.02

2.03
2.04
2.05

2.06
2.07
2.08
2.09

10.00 Woodwork

10.01 Timber for carcassing work to be of GS or MGS grade as laid down in BS 4978

10.02 Timber for joinery shall be a species approved by the architect, selected from and conforming to BS 1186.

10.03 Moisture content of all timber at time of fixing to be appropriate to the situation and conditions in which it is used. To this effect all timber and components will be protected from the weather prior to their use.

10.04

10.05

10.06

10.18 Construct the first floor using 50 mm × 200 mm sawn softwood joists at 400 mm centres supported on mild steel hangers.

Provide 75 mm × 200 mm trimmer and trimming around stairwell, securely tusk-tenoned together.

Provide and fix to joists 38 mm × 38 mm sawn softwood herring-bone strutting at 1.8 m maximum intervals.

Provide and fix galvanized restraint straps at 2 m maximum intervals to act as positive ties between the joists and walls.

10.19 Provide and secret fix around the trimmed stairwell opening a 25 mm Brazilian mahogany apron lining, tongued to a matching 25 mm × 100 mm nosing.

10.20 Provide and lay to the whole of the first floor 19 mm × 100 mm prepared softwood tongued-and-grooved floor boarding, each board well cramped up and surface nailed with two 50 mm flooring brads to each joist. The nail heads to be well punched down.

Specification

STUDY THE SCHEDULE

Schedule

This is a contract document that is used to record repetitive design information about a range of similar components e.g. doors, ironmongery, finishes and sanitary ware, etc. There will also be a schedule which lists all of the drawings related to the job.

Description	Plot 2				Plot 6				Plot 7				Plot 8				Plot 9				Plot 10				Plot 12			
	Kitchen	Cloaks	Bath	En-suite	Kitchen	Cloaks	Bath	En-suite	Kitchen	Cloaks	Bath	En-suite	Kitchen	Cloaks	Bath	En-suite	Kitchen	Cloaks	Bath	En-suite	Kitchen	Cloaks	Bath	En-suite	Kitchen	Cloaks	Bath	En-suite
ITEM (see range)																												
Inset sink	×				×				×				×				×				×				×			
Waste disposal unit	×								×												×							
Close Couple WC		×	×	×		×	×	×		×	×	×		×	×	×		×	×	×		×	×	×		×	×	×
Bidet				×				×				×				×				×				×				×
Pedestal wash basin			×	×			×	×			×	×			×	×			×	×			×	×			×	×
Wall hung corner basin		×				×				×				×				×				×				×		
Bath			×				×				×				×				×				×				×	
Shower tray				×				×				×				×				×				×				×
STYLE (see range)																												
Anne							×	×														×		×			×	
Sarah		×				×				×				×	×	×										×		
James			×	×							×	×						×	×	×			×					×
Single drainer					×								×				×											
Double drainer	×								×												×				×			
COLOUR																												
Penthouse Red							×	×																×				
Indian ivory						×					×	×				×							×					
Honeysuckle				×	×										×							×				×	×	×
White		×								×				×				×	×	×								
BRASS WORK																												
Chrome plated	×	×	×	×	×	×			×	×	×	×	×	×			×	×	×	×	×	×	×		×	×	×	×
Gold plated							×	×							×	×								×				

Notes

BBS DESIGN

JOB TITLE
Lakeside Estate

DRAWING TITLE
Schedule for sanitary appliances

JOB NO.		DRAWING NO.	
SCALE	DATE	DRAWN	CHECKED

Learning task

Using the schedule for sanitary appliances, estate plan and house plan, complete the order/requisition form for the sanitary appliances required for plot number 6.

These are required on site for installation on the 15 March 1992 at the latest.

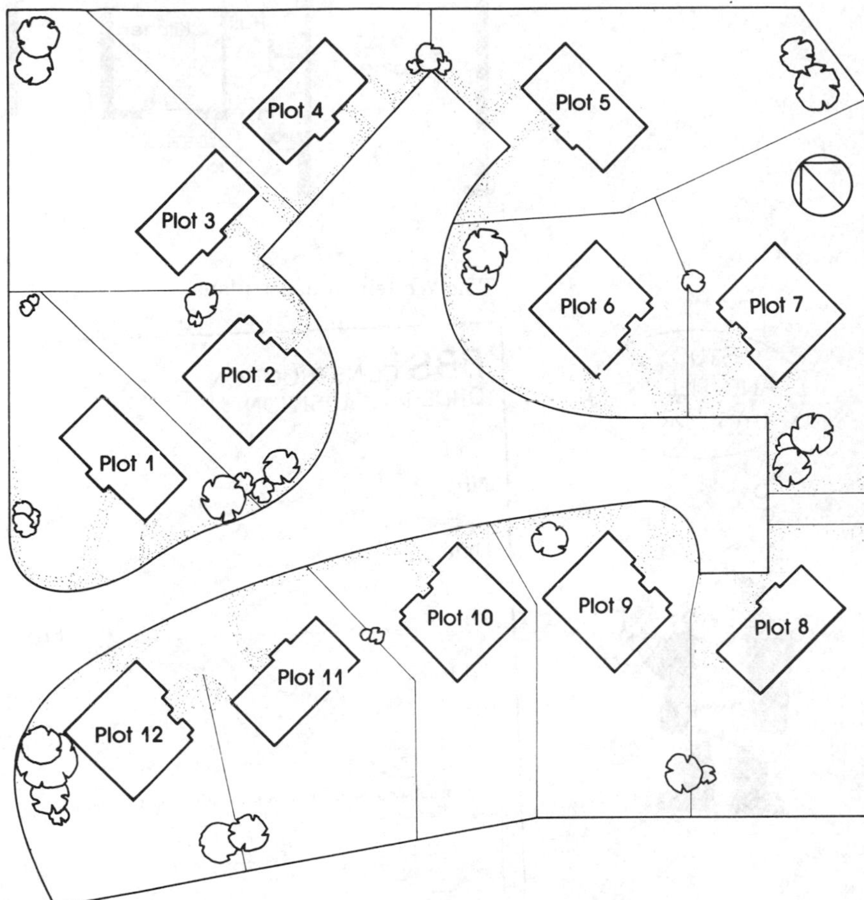

Estate plan

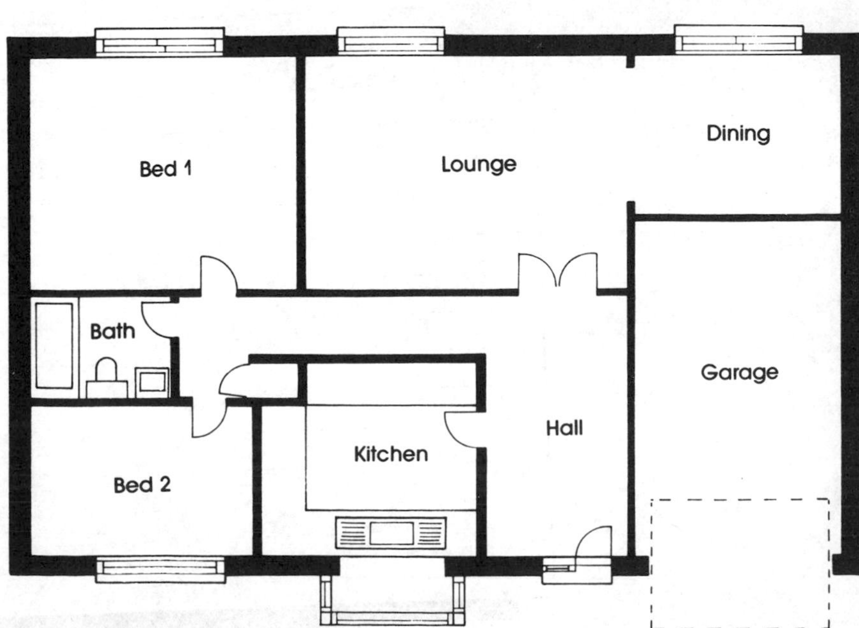

The lakeside bungalow plan

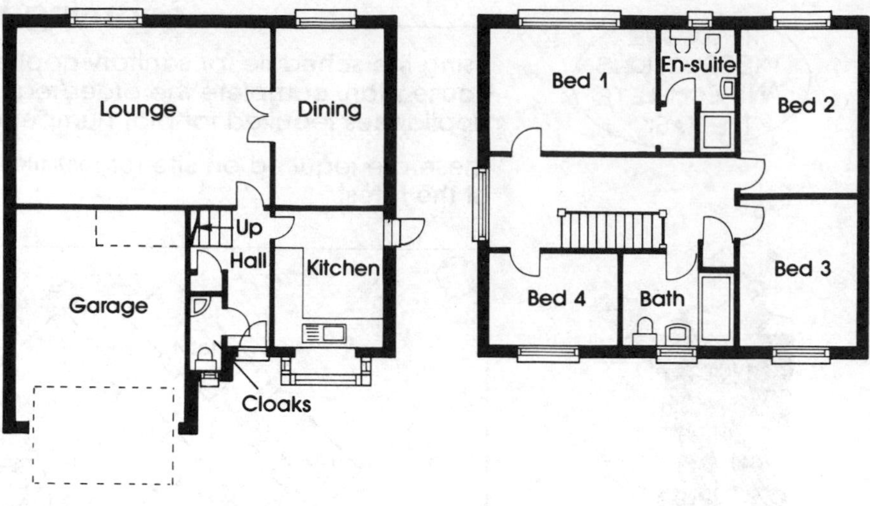

The Whiteman house plans

BBS CONSTRUCTION
ORDER/REQUISITION

Registered office

No. ______________________

Date ______________________

To ______________________

Address ______________________

From ______________________

Site address ______________________

Please supply or order for delivery to the above site the following:

Description	Quantity	Rate	Date required by

Site manager/foreman ______________________

Note Please advise site within 24 hours of request if order cannot be fulfilled by the date required

Bill of quantities (BOQ)

This is a document prepared by the quantity surveyor. It gives a description and measure of quantities of labour, materials and other items required to carry out a building contract. It is based on the architect's working drawings, specifications and schedules and forms part of the contract documents.

ITEM	DESCRIPTION	QUANTITY	UNIT	RATE	AMOUNT
	Preliminaries Name of parties Client: Mr W. Whiteman, Whiteman Enterprises, Engineering House, Bedford				£
	Architect BBS Design				
A					
B					

ITEM	DESCRIPTION	QUANTITY	UNIT	RATE	AMOUNT
	Preambles woodwork (cont.)				£
A	Impregnated timber is timber which has been pressure impregnated with an approved preservative by a specialist firm. Any timber cut on the site after treatment must have a liberal brush application of the same preservative in accordance with the manufacturer's instructions.				
B					
C					
D					
E					
F					
G					

ITEM	DESCRIPTION	QUANTITY	UNIT	RATE	AMOUNT
	Super structure (upper floor) Woodwork Impregnated sawn softwood				£
A	50 mm × 200 mm joist	85	M		
B	75 mm × 200 mm joist	7	M		
C					
D					
E					
F					
G					
H					
J					
K					
L					
M					

ITEM	DESCRIPTION	QUANTITY	UNIT	RATE	AMOUNT	
	Internal doors (cont.)					
	Ironmongery				£	
	Supply and fix the following ironmongery as described with matching screws to softwood or plywood faced doors. *Note*: references refer to BBS catalogue no. 6b					
A	*Pair* 100 mm pressed steel butt hinges (1.47)	2	No			
B	*Pair* 75 mm pressed steel butt hinges (1.48)	4.5	No			
C	*Pair* 75 mm brass butt hinges (1.23)	1	No			
D	Mortise lock/latch (2.14)	2	No			
E	Mortise latch (2.15)	6	No			
F	Mortise lock/latch furniture (3.14)	2	No			
G	Mortise latch furniture (3.15)	6	No			
H	Coat hook (6.25)	2	No			
J	Provide the P.C. sum of *three hundred and fifty pounds* £350 for the supply and installation by a specialist subcontractor of two overhead garage doors.				350	00
K	*Add* for expenses and profit.			%		
L	Include the provisional sum of *one hundred and fifty pounds* £150 for contingencies.				150	00
	Carried to Collection			£		

Contract documents

These various documents together form the legal contract. Normally they consist of the architect's working drawings, specification, schedules, bill of quantities and the conditions of contract. A standard document is normally used but it could be specially prepared.

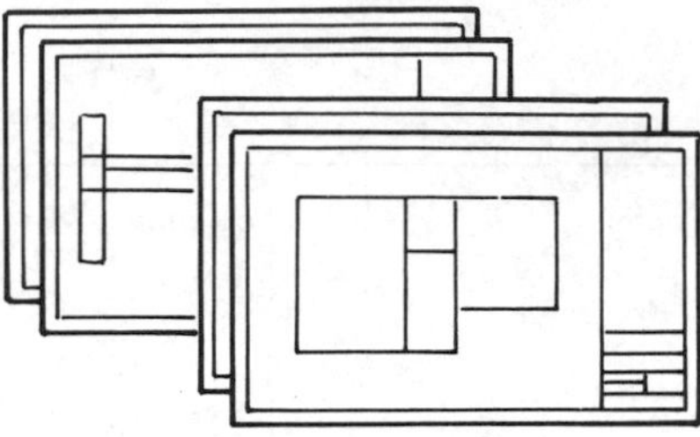

Architect's working drawings

Specification

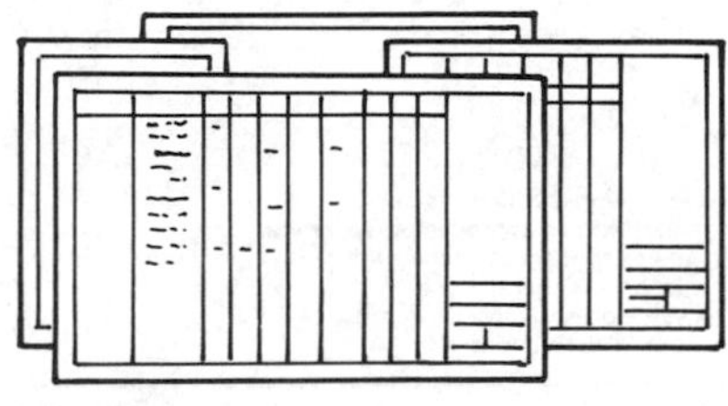

Schedules

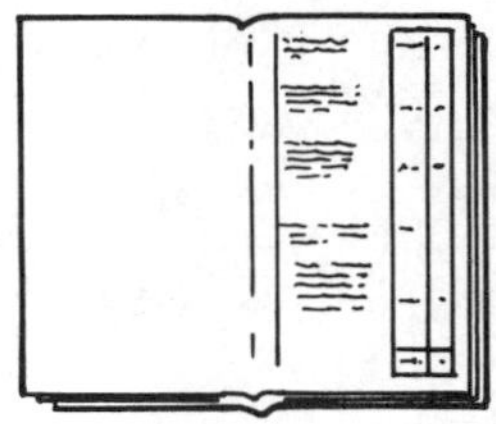

Bill of quantities

Conditions of contract

Delivery notes and records

When materials and plant are delivered to a site, someone is required to sign the driver's delivery note. A careful check must be made to ensure that all the materials are there and undamaged. Any missing or damaged goods must be clearly indicated on the delivery note and followed up by a letter to the supplier. Many suppliers send out an advice note prior to delivery which states details of the materials and the expected delivery date. This enables the site management to make arrangements for unloading and storage. Delivery records are often completed to provide a record of all the materials received on site. These are normally filled in and sent to the organisation's head office along with a copy of the delivery notes on a weekly basis. This record is used to confirm goods have been delivered before paying suppliers' invoices.

Learning task

You have supervised the delivery of materials shown on the note on the next page. On checking the delivery, only 48 lengths of 50 × 50 were received and several of the shrink-wrapped hardwood packages had splits in them. Sign the delivery note and make any comments you think applicable.

BBS SUPPLIES
DELIVERY NOTE

Registered office
Brett House
1 Hagely Road
Birmingham
B11 N4

No. 8914

Date 15 MARCH 1992

Delivered to
T. JOYCEE
25 DAWNCRAFT WAY
STENSON DERBY D.70

Invoice to
FELLOWS, MORTON PLC
JOSHER STREET
BIRMINGHAM B21

Please receive in good condition the undermentioned goods

SAWN TREATED SOFTWOOD
50 OFF 25 X 50 X 3600
50 OFF 50 X 50 X 4.800

KILN SEASONED HARDWOOD
25 OFF 25 X 150 X 2400 (REBATED WINDOW SILLS)

(SHRINK-WRAPPED IN PLASTIC)

Received by

Remarks

Note Claims for shortages and damage will not be considered unless recorded on this sheet.

STUDY AND FILL IN THIS FORM

Complete the deliveries record for the last order.

BBS CONSTRUCTION
DELIVERIES RECORD

Week no. P3 WK3 Date MARCH 92

Job title STENSON FIELDS

Registered office
Brett House
1 Hagely Road
Birmingham
B11 N4

Delivery note no.	Date	Supplier	Description of delivery	For office use only	
				Rate	Value
241	14/3/92	G. BOGGS	SANITARY WARE		
1535	14/3/92	I. BLUNDER	READY-MIX CONCRETE		
			Total		

Site manager/foreman ______________________

Note Send weekly to head office with delivery notes

Questions for you

1. State why scale drawings are used in the construction industry.

2. Explain the purpose of a range drawing.

3. Explain the purpose of a specification.

4. What action should you take if a materials delivery does not match the delivery note?

5. Explain why graphical symbols are used on drawings.

6. State **TWO** main details shown on a site plan.

7. What would 5 mm on a drawing to a scale of 1 : 20 actually represent full size?

Messages

Much communication within and between organisations takes place by means of forms. The issuer of the form is able to ask precisely the information required and in the desired order. There is normally no opportunity to waffle or give irrelevant details.

When you fill in a form for any reason, remember the following basic rules:

- Read the instructions carefully (e.g. do they ask for handwritten, BLOCK CAPITALS, or a black pen, etc.
- Read the questions carefully (do not squash in an answer if there is an opportunity to give that information elsewhere).
- Ensure your writing is legible.
- If your name is Peter Stephen Brett, then your surname, family or last name is Brett; your forename, first name or Christian name is Peter; your other name is Stephen; your initials are PSB.
  Where a maiden name is asked for this would be a married person's surname before marriage.
- Complete all dates, times, etc. accurately.
- Delete inappropriate details as asked.
- Do not leave blanks, always write 'not applicable' or 'N/A'.
- Do not forget to sign the form if required. This is normally your initials and surname. This is your signature.
- Do not write where you see these:
  For official use only
  For office use only
  For store use
  For company use, etc.
- Finally, read through the form again to ensure all sections have been completed correctly.

PLEASE PRINT FULL NAME

BLOCK LETTERS ONLY

B CUSTOMER TO COMPLETE (BLOCK CAPITALS PLEASE)

When completing this form ensure the details show clearly on both copies.

Mr/~~Mrs~~/~~Ms~~ P. S. BRETT

Delivery 70 SHALIMAR RD.

Address STEPPING BROOK

NORTHAMPTON

Full Postcode NN7 8WL

Tel: Home (STD 0604) No. 743521

Office (STD 021) No. 345001

I understand that the trusses will be manufactured to the correct sizes based upon the dimensions I have provided and I accept responsibility for the dimensions.

CUSTOMER'S SIGNATURE

PSBrett

DATE 15/3/92

ORDER FORM

FOR MADE TO MEASURE REPLACEMENT WINDOWS

When completing this form ensure the details show clearly on all copies.
MR/MRS/MS .... (INITIALS) .... (SURNAME) ....
DELIVERY ADDRESS ....
....
.... FULL POSTCODE ....
Please indicate where you would like the goods left, if delivered in your absence.
....
....
TELEPHONE: HOME (STD ....) No ....
OFFICE (STD ....) No ....
I understand that the windows will be manufactured to the correct sizes based upon the dimensions I have provided and I accept responsibility for the dimensions.

CUSTOMER'S SIGNATURE .... DATE ....

STORE USE ONLY

STORE [0| |]

DATE OF ORDER ....
PURCHASE ORDER No. ....
DRL No. ....
ADMIN. CHECKED BY ....
RECEIPT No. ....
TENDER TYPE: CHEQUE/CREDIT/CASH

Blue - Order Copy
White - Store Copy
Green - Goods Inwards Copy
Yellow - Customer Copy

SEE REVERSE SIDE FOR ORDERING INSTRUCTIONS AND GUIDANCE (Enter required details and complete all sections)

SKETCH YOUR WINDOWS SHOWING DESIGNS AND DIMENSIONS HERE. N.B. ALWAYS VIEWED FROM THE OUTSIDE
(See HOW TO ORDER WINDOWS notes for opening lights min/max)
(Please note that our range of Made to Measure Windows vary in specification to our standard stock range.)

Do you require sills? YES ☐ NO ☐
Do you intend to use these windows in conjunction with our range of standard windows? YES ☐ NO ☐
Have you ordered made to measure windows from us before? ☐ If so, please state approx. date of order ....

Memoranda or memos

These are forms of written communication which are used within an organisation. They would not be sent out to customers or suppliers.

When you send a memo for any reason, remember the following points:

- Be brief but use formal English
- Deal with one topic only
- May be hand- or typewritten

BBS CONSTRUCTION **MEMO**

From JOHN PESSAL To IAN CARPENTER

Subject POWER TOOLS Date 16 JANUARY 1992

Message

I HAVE MADE AN ORDER FOR THE POWER TOOLS. THEY SHOULD BE WITH YOU BY THE 20 JANUARY. TRUST THIS IS OKAY.

JOHN.

Learning task

Complete the following memo to Christine Baldwin advising her that you will be able to attend the Safety Meeting next Friday.

READ THE INSTRUCTIONS AND COMPLETE THE TASK

BBS CONSTRUCTION **MEMO**

From ______________________ To ______________________

Subject ______________________ Date ______________________

Message

Letters

Letters provide a permanent record of communication between organisations and individuals. They can be handwritten, but formal business letters give a better impression of the organisation if they are typed. They should be written using simple concise language. The tone should be polite and business-like, even if it is a letter of complaint. They must be clearly constructed with each fresh point contained in a separate paragraph for easy understanding. When you write a letter for any reason, remember the following basic rules:

- Your own address should be written in full, complete with the postcode.
- Include the inside address. This is the title of the person (plus name if known) and the name and address of the organisation you are writing to. This should be the same as appears on the envelope.
- Write the date in full, e.g. 30 January 1992.

- Greetings. Use 'Dear Sir/Madam' if you are unsure of the sex of the person you are writing to, or 'Dear Sir' or 'Dear Madam' as applicable. Use the person's name if you know it.
- Endings. Use 'Yours faithfully' for all letters unless you have used the person's name in the greeting, in which case use 'Yours sincerely'.
- Signature. Sign below the ending. Your name and status should be printed below the signature, if applicable.

40 St.James Road
Great Barr
Birmingham
BB4 5EL

15th March 1992

Your address

Inside address of who letter is going to

The Personnel Manager
BBS Supplies
Brett House
1 Hagley Road
Birmingham
B11 N4

Dear Sir — Greeting

Thank you for your letter of 11th March 1992, inviting me for interview for the position of Trainee Store Person.

I look forward to meeting you on Friday 22nd March 1992 at 10.30 a.m.

Yours faithfully — Ending

C. White

C.White — Signature

Learning task

Imagine that you are an employee of Permabuild and write a letter of complaint to your materials supplier concerning the delivery you received on 15 March 1992. (See page 92.)

Permabuild Ltd

Ridge House
Norton Road
Cheltenham
GL59 1DB

Telephone

Telephones play an important communication role both within an organisation and to customers and suppliers. Its advantage over a written message is the speed with which people are put in touch with one another.

Telephone manner Remember that you cannot be seen, you will have no facial expressions or other body language to help make yourself understood. The tone, volume and pace of your voice is important. Speak clearly and loud enough to be heard without shouting; sound cheerful, speak at a speed at which the recipient can take down any message, key words or phrases that you are trying to relay.

Making calls If you initiate a call you are more likely to be in control of the conversation and when you have achieved your objective you will be in the best position to end the call without causing offence. Make notes before you begin. Have times, dates and other necessary information ready. Write down your name and address before making a call if you find it difficult to spell out words 'from your head'. The call may take the following form:

'Good morning' or 'Good afternoon'.
'This is (your name) speaking, of (organisation)'.
Give the name of the person you wish to speak to, if a specific individual is required.
State the reason for your call.
Keep the call brief.
Thank the recipient, even if the call did not produce the results required.

Receiving a call A good telephone manner is as vital as when making a call. The call may take the following form:

'Good morning' or 'Good afternoon'; (organisation) (your name) speaking, how can I help you?'
If the call is not for you and the person required is unavailable ask politely if you can take a message.

Telephone messages It is important that you understand what someone is saying to you on the telephone, and you may make notes of the conversation. However, when the message is not for you it is *essential* that you make written notes during the call, even though you may be seeing the person soon and be able to give the message verbally.

Always make sure that the message contains all the necessary details. Any vagueness or omission of details could lead to problems.

Joe has to leave a message for Sid about two telephone calls. If all he writes is:

Sid is left with the problem of finding out:

- How much paint each wants.
- Which colour each wants.

A separate message for each in the following form would be much clearer.

Telephone Message

Date 15 MARCH Time 0945

Message for SID

Message from (Name) JUDY

(Address) STENSON FIELDS
CONTRACT DERBY

(Telephone) 084 445 733

Message CAN YOU BRING TWO 5 LITRE CANS OF BLUE GLOSS PAINT WHEN YOU ATTEND THE SITE MEETING TOMORROW
MANY THANKS

Message taken by JOE

READ THE INSTRUCTIONS AND COMPLETE THE TASK

Learning task

At 1030 on Monday 14 March you take a telephone call for the general foreman Helen Oakes, from Vic Aston the carpentry sub-contractor, based in Birmingham, telephone number 021 354 687.

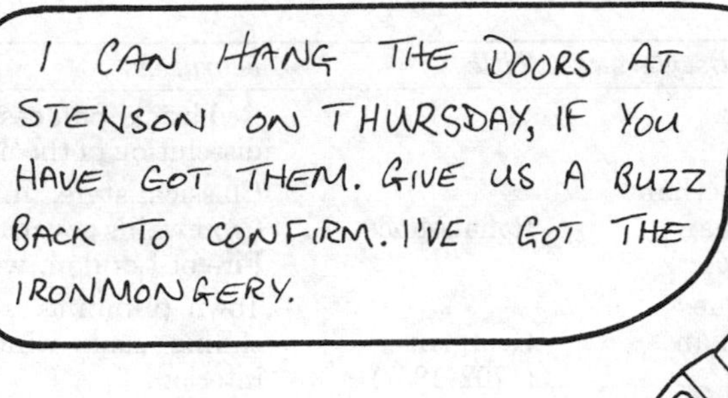

Use this message to fill in the form.

Telephone Message

Date .... Time ....

Message for ....

Message from (Name) ....

(Address) ....

....

(Telephone) ....

Message ....

....

....

....

....

Message taken by ....

Extracting information

Throughout your working life at various levels in industry, you will have to make decisions and solve problems. To do this effectively you will have to consult various sources of information. Specialist information may be obtained from Regulations, Standards, manufacturers and Trade Development Association publications, textbooks and periodicals.

Date	*Period/style*	*Title*	*Features*
1485–1558	Tudor		Red brick, palaces, timber-box frame, Reformation and dissolution of the monasteries, decorative brick chimneys
1558–1603 1603–1625 1625–1702	Elizabethan Jacobean Stuart	Renaissance	Classical style, numerous large windows, the Civil War, Cromwell's government, restoration of monarchy, Great Fire of London, window tax
1695–1720 1720–1760 1760–1800 1800–1837	Baroque Palladian Adam Regency	Georgian (1702–1837)	Town planning, squares and terraces of fine houses, sliding sash windows, stucco, brick tax, elaborate interiors
1837–1901	Victorian		Battle of styles, Gothic revival, Crystal Palace, Industrial Revolution, spread of industrial towns, back-to-back housing, cast iron, Portland cement, monumental public buildings, electric lighting, telephone, Public Health Act, tap water and outside lavatories become common
1901–1910 1910–onwards	Edwardian Modern	Twentieth century	Introduction of garden cities, first Town Planning Act, two World Wars, jerry-building, ribbon development, new towns, reinforced concrete, steel frame, high-rise construction, system building, council housing, increasing comfort in housing

Learning task

Study the table above and extract the following information.

List the main features of the Tudor period.

____

____

____

Name the period in which electric lighting was introduced.

____

List the following architectural periods under either Georgian or Renaissance:

Baroque	Elizabethan
Stuart	Palladian
Regency	Adam
Jacobean	

Georgian	*Renaissance*

Personal communications

Yourself and work colleagues

It is necessary, in order for companies to function effectively, that they establish and maintain good working relationships within their organisational structure. This can be achieved by good co-operation and communication between the various sections and individual workers; good working conditions (pay, holidays, status, security, future opportunities and a pleasant safe working environment); and finally by nurturing a good team spirit, where people are motivated, rewarded for their success and allowed to work on their own initiative under supervision for the good of the company as a whole. Most companies have a hierarchical structure, which you have studied earlier in this package. Your working relationships with your immediate colleagues is equally important to the team spirit and overall success. Remember, always plan your work to ensure ease of operation, co-ordination and co-operation with other members of the workforce.

Customers

Remember, the customers pay your wages and they should be treated with respect. You should be polite at all times, even with those that are 'difficult'. Listen carefully to their wishes and pass to a higher authority in the company anything you cannot deal with to the customer's satisfaction.

Always treat customers' property with the utmost care. Use dust sheets to protect carpets and furnishings when working internally. Clean up periodically and make a special effort when the job is complete. Remember, when working in their property you are a guest and you should treat everything accordingly. If any problem occurs contact your supervisor.

Ensure good standards of personal hygiene especially when working in occupied customers' premises. A smelly, dirty workperson will make the customer think the work will be poor. This may cause them to withdraw their offer of employment or may result in further work being given to another company.

- Wash frequently.
- Use deodorant if you have a smelly perspiration problem.
- Wear clean overalls and have them washed at least once a week.
- Take off your muddy boots etc. when working internally on customers' premises.

Questions for you

8. State the purpose of the national code in a telephone number.

9. Who should you contact if any problem occurs in a customer's home?

WORD-SQUARE SEARCH

Hidden in the word-square are the following 20 words associated with '*Communications*'. You may find the words written forwards, backwards, up, down or diagonally.

Bill	Communication
Sketch	Scale
Drawings	Range
Messages	Oblique
Schedules	Orthographic
Plans	Specification
Memo	Customer
Letter	Component
Symbol	Contract
Assembly	

Draw a ring around the words, or line in using a highlight pen thus:

EXAMPLE

EXAMPLE

P	C	R	Y	L	B	M	E	S	S	A	D	P	S	C	A	L	E
C	L	R	I	S	I	E	S	A	L	T	B	R	Y	O	T	E	F
C	R	A	S	L	L	M	F	D	N	D	H	O	M	M	P	P	G
O	I	C	N	V	L	O	A	E	L	C	P	H	B	M	E	O	H
N	A	D	D	S	Y	A	N	A	T	O	C	I	O	U	H	R	A
T	U	I	L	N	T	O	T	E	G	T	C	B	L	N	E	T	T
R	A	N	G	E	P	A	K	A	O	T	D	I	A	I	L	E	E
A	T	W	V	M	E	S	S	A	G	E	S	T	H	C	M	D	S
C	A	T	O	S	S	S	Y	D	I	E	O	I	T	A	E	B	G
T	C	C	O	C	C	T	R	U	C	T	I	O	N	T	T	C	N
X	O	O	R	T	H	O	G	R	A	P	H	I	C	I	S	A	I
U	B	N	E	L	E	R	T	R	S	L	A	F	A	O	T	I	W
R	L	S	P	V	D	D	A	C	C	I	D	E	N	N	P	E	A
O	I	T	V	C	U	S	T	O	M	E	R	D	I	C	C	A	R
L	Q	R	D	E	L	B	N	H	I	B	I	T	T	I	O	N	D
K	U	U	T	I	E	L	E	T	T	E	R	S	O	D	C	D	V
F	E	C	T	A	S	B	M	L	A	D	E	D	E	R	S	I	E
C	S	P	E	C	I	F	I	C	A	T	I	O	N	D	E	N	T

4 Scaffolding

Using scaffolding

Scaffolding is a temporary structure which is used in order to carry out certain building operations at height. It must, as applicable, provide a safe means of access to heights and a safe working platform.

Scaffolding should only be erected, altered and dismantled by a trained scaffolder. Craft operatives have to work on scaffolding 'safely'. It is therefore essential that you have an understanding of scaffolding principles, types, materials and statutory regulations.

The following are some of the official publications which deal with scaffolding. They are recommended for further reading.

The Construction (Working Places) Regulations, 1966
The Construction (Lifting Operations) Regulations, 1961
BS 1139 1982: Metal Scaffolding.
BS 2483 1981: Timber Scaffold Boards.

Tubular scaffolding

Materials must conform to the regulations given in the publications on the previous page.

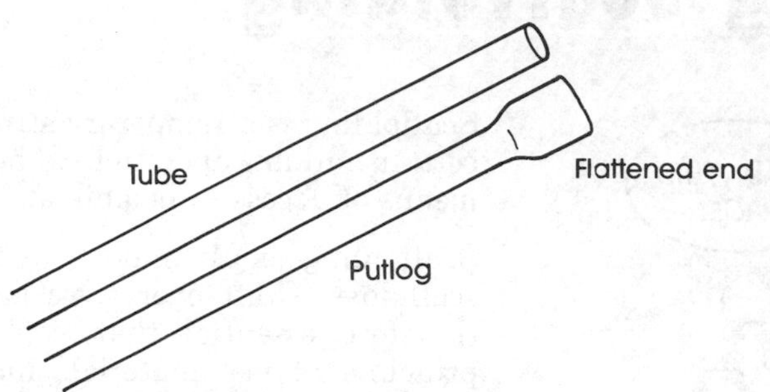

Scaffold tubes

These may be either tubular steel or tubular aluminium. Both types have an outside diameter of 48 mm. However they should not be used in the same scaffold, as aluminium tubes deflect more than the tubes made from steel under the same loading conditions.

Putlog – a type of short tube with flattened end, to bear in a brick joint; used for putlog scaffolds.

Scaffold fittings

These may be manufactured from either steel or aluminium. They are both normally suitable for use with both types of tube, unless the manufacturer or supplier states otherwise.

Double coupler – a one-piece coupler which connects two scaffold tubes together at right angles.

Universal coupler – connects two scaffold tubes together at right angles or parallel to each other.

Swivel coupler – a one-piece coupler which connects two scaffold tubes together at any angle.

Putlog coupler – a non-loadbearing one-piece coupler which connects putlogs to ledgers.

Joint pin – an internal fitting which expands and grips against the wall of the tube, used for joining two vertical scaffold tubes end to end.

Sleeve coupler – an external fitting used for joining two horizontal or bracing scaffold tubes end to end.

Base plate – a steel plate 150 mm square with an integral spigot, used for distributing loads from standards and has fixing holes for nailing to sole plates.

Adjustable base plate – a base plate for use on uneven ground. It incorporates a robust screw thread which enables adjustment for levelling.

Reveal pin – inserted into the end of a short piece of scaffold tube. When adjusted it forms a rigid fixing member in a window reveal or other opening.

Putlog end – attached over the end of a scaffold tube to convert it into a putlog.

Guard board clip – connects a guard board or toe board to a scaffold standard.

Gin wheel – used for raising and lowering equipment from a scaffold. Incorporates a swivel ring at the top which completely encircles the tube for maximum safety.

Castor wheel – used for mobile towers, must be fitted with a locking device or brake.

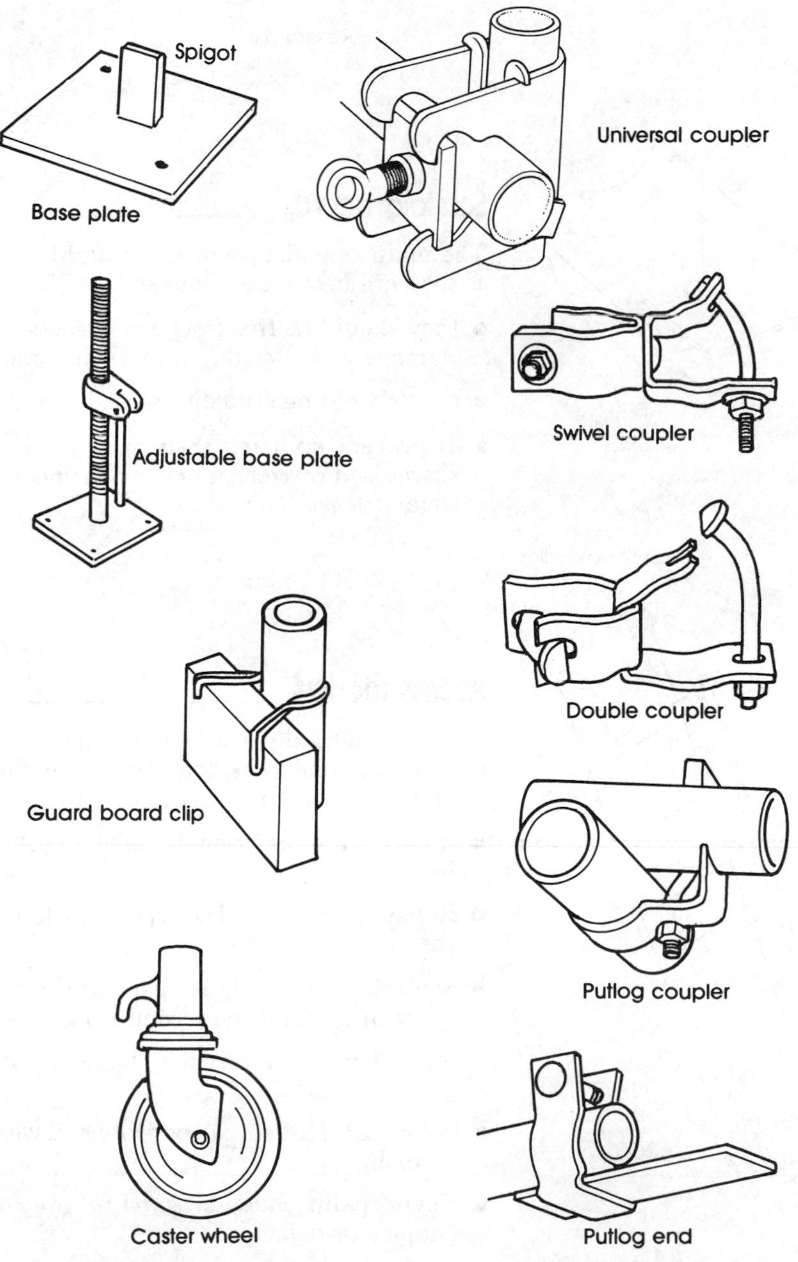

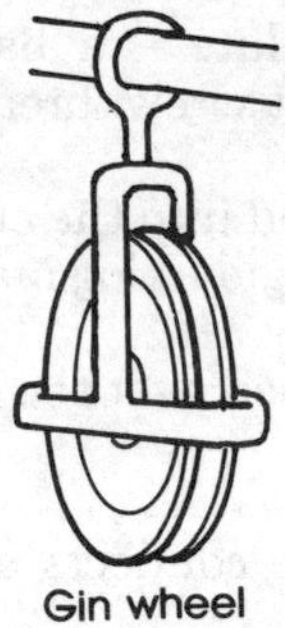
Gin wheel

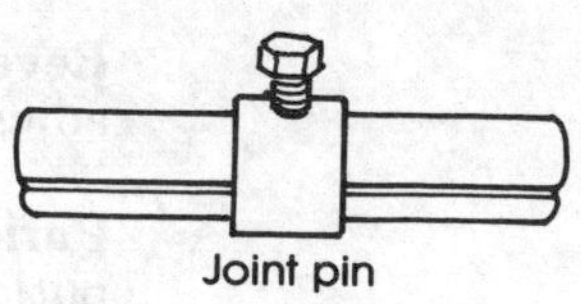
Joint pin

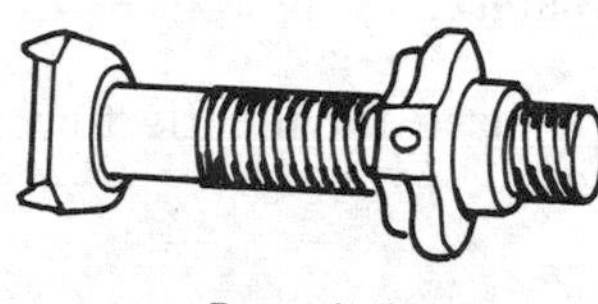
Reveal pin

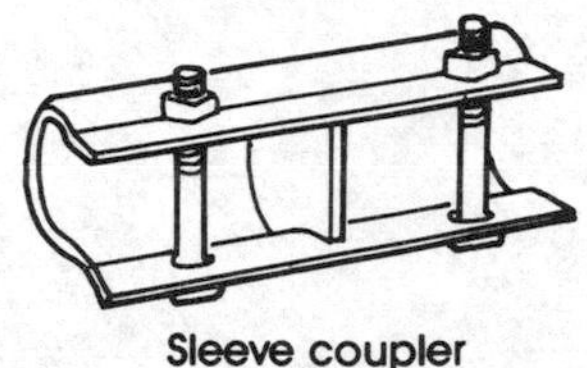
Sleeve coupler

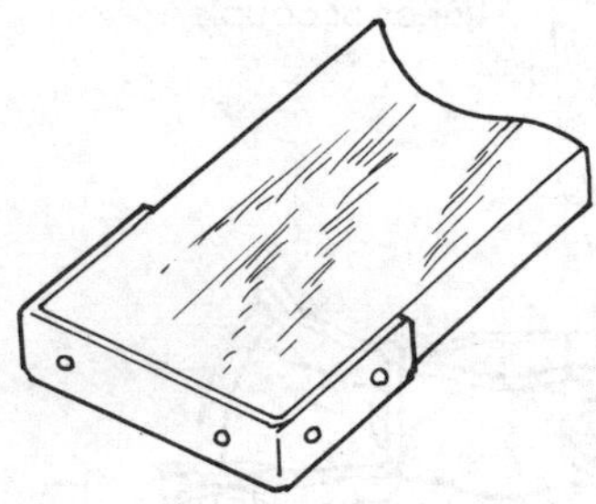

Scaffold boards

The main considerations for scaffold boards are that:

- they are best made from spruce, fir, redwood or whitewood
- they should be free from any defects, such as splits, checks, shakes or damage which could affect their strength
- they should be straight grained, not twisted or warped
- to prevent splitting their ends should be bound with galvanised or sheradised (corrosion protection) hoop iron, which extends along each edge at least 150 mm.

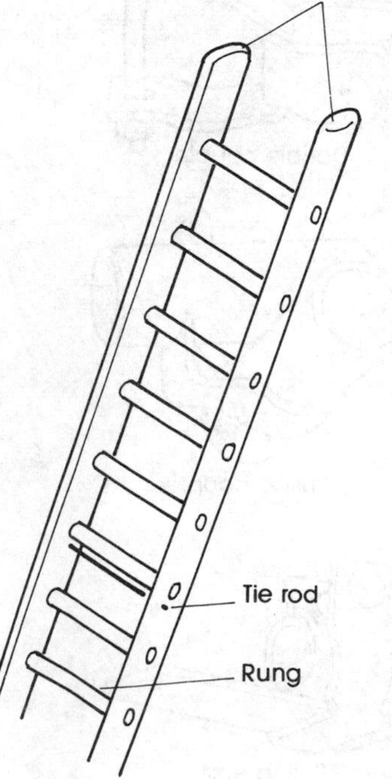

Access ladders

These are normally pole ladders, and are made from one piece of European whitewood which has been cut down the middle. This is to ensure the ladder has an even strength and flexibility.

- Rungs are either round or rectangular and made from oak, birch or hickory.
- Rungs at the top and bottom of the ladder must be at least 100 mm from the ends of the stiles.
- Steel tie rods should be fitted at intervals of not more than nine rungs apart and under the second rung from each end of the ladder.
- Steel reinforcing wire may be incorporated in the edge of the stile for extra strength.
- Before use, ladders can be protected with a coat of clear, exterior quality varnish.
- **Never** paint ladders as paint may conceal potentially dangerous damage or defects.

Types of tube scaffolding

Putlog scaffolds

These are often known as either bricklayers' scaffold or single scaffold. They are normally used when constructing new brick buildings and consist of a single row of vertical standards which are connected together by horizontal ledgers. Putlogs are coupled to the ledgers and are built into the wall as the brickwork proceeds. This type of scaffold obtains most of its support and stability from the building.

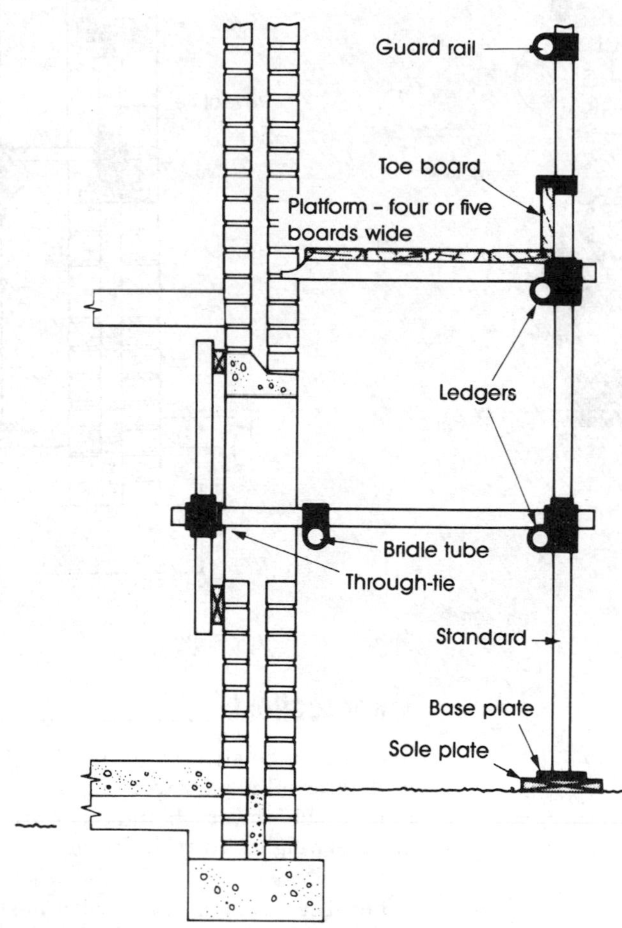

Independent scaffolds

These are sometimes called double scaffolds as they are constructed using a double row of standards. This type of scaffold carries its own weight and the full weight of all loads imposed upon it, but it is not completely independent. It must be suitably tied to the building for stability.

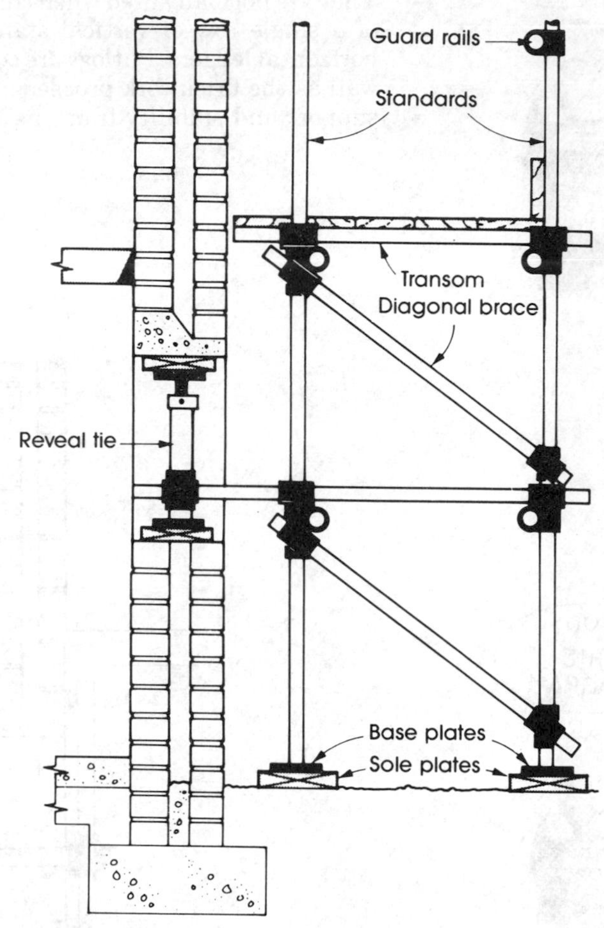

Tower scaffold

These may be either static or mobile. They are suitable for both internal and external use for work up to about 6 m in height. For work above this height the tower should be tied into the building or be fitted with counterweights to stabilise it.

When the tower is fitted with castors, these should incorporate brakes which lock the wheels. The height is limited according to the size of the tower's base. For internal use the maximum height should not exceed $3\frac{1}{2}$ times the shorter base dimension.

For external use the height is restricted to three times this dimension. Outriggers which increase the base dimension can be used to permit additional height.

Tower scaffolds must only be used on firm, level ground. Mobile towers must never be moved while people or equipment are on them.

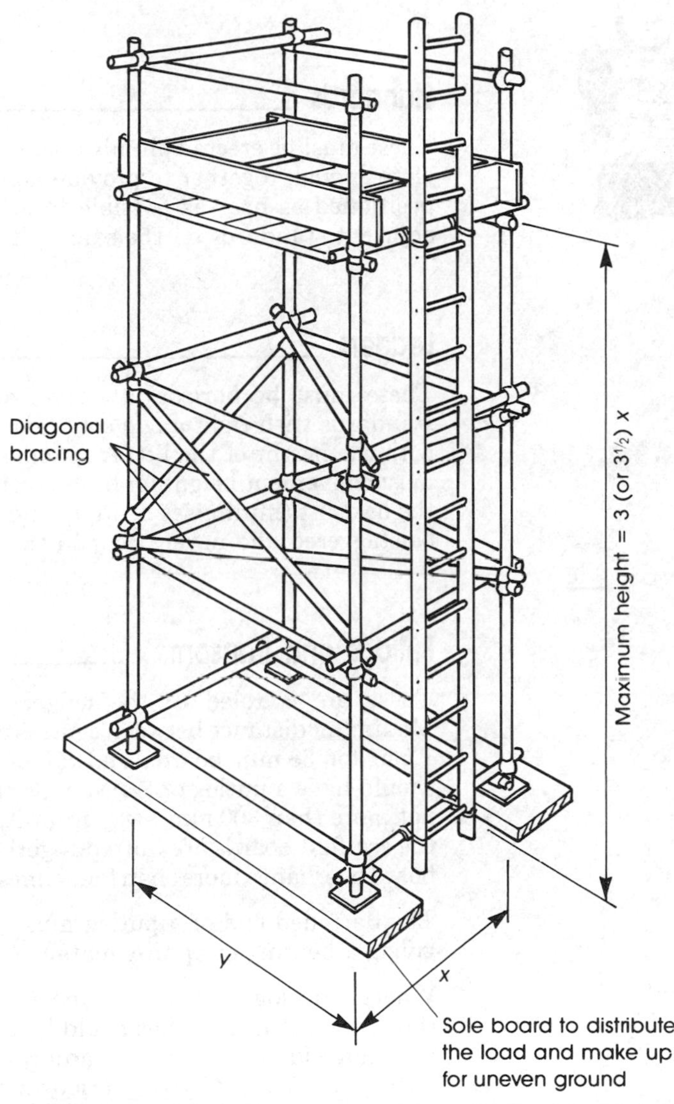

Static tower

Scaffold components

Base

A good foundation for a scaffold is essential, it should be made using at least 35 mm × 220 mm sole plates laid on a firm, level base of well-rammed earth or hardcore. Base plates must be fixed to the sole plates under every standard. Bricks, blocks or timber offcuts must not be used.

Standards

These must be erected plumb or lean slightly towards the building, spaced close enough together to provide adequate support, joints staggered and positioned as near as possible to a ledger (joints should never occur in adjacent standards on the same lift).

Ledgers

These must be horizontally level and connected on the inside of the standards with right angle couplers. The spacing between ledgers varies with the height of the lift. A spacing of 1.2 m to 1.5 m is found to be the most convenient height for bricklayers to build a wall before moving up to the next lift (minimises bending and stretching). Joints in ledgers should be staggered and never occur in the same bay.

Putlogs and transoms

These are coupled to the ledgers at centres of about 1.2 m apart. Maximum distance between centres depends on the board thickness used: 1.5 m for 38 mm boards and 2.6 m for 50 mm boards. Each standard should have a putlog or transom as close as possible to it and in any case not more than 300 mm away from it. Double putlogs are required where the scaffold boards are butted together. These must be placed so that no board overhangs more than four times its thickness or less than 50 mm.

The flattened end of a putlog must be pushed right into the brick joint giving a bearing of approximately 75 mm.

Where a putlog is required opposite an opening in the building, a short tube called a bridle tube should be clamped with right angle couplers to the underside of the putlogs adjacent to the opening. The intermediate putlog can then be fixed to the ledger and bridle using right angle couplers.

Tying in to a building

Putlog scaffold

It is most important that this is tied in correctly as putlogs can easily work loose in green (newly laid) brickwork. All ties should be of the through type, one tie for each 32 m^2 of scaffold area (sheeted scaffolds will require more ties due to increased wind resistance: one tie per 25 m^2). All couplers used for tying should be right angle couplers and the ties should be next to, or as close as possible to, the intersection of a standard and ledger.

Until the ties become effective, temporary rakers should be fixed to each alternate standard, to stabilise the scaffold.

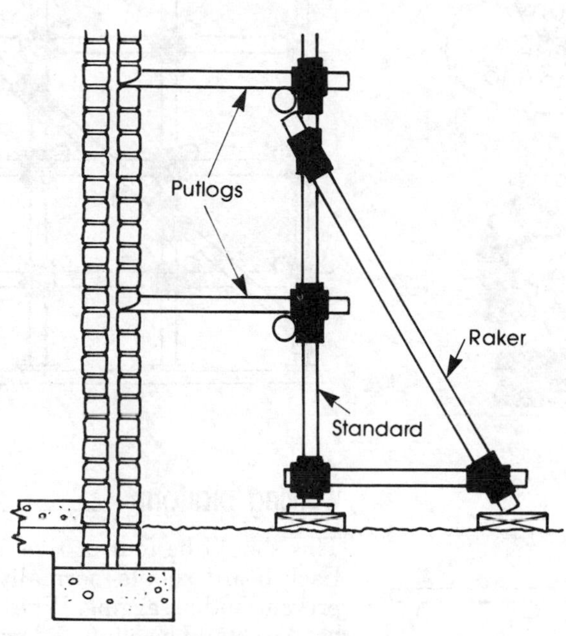

Independent scaffold

Tying is essential in order to prevent the scaffold moving away from or into the building. One tie is required for each 32 m^2 of scaffold area. Again, sheeted scaffolds will require more ties due to increased wind resistance. Ties can either be reveal ties, through ties, box ties or ties provided by casting or drilled in anchorages.

Again, until the ties become effective, temporary rakers should be fixed to each alternate standard, to stabilise the scaffold.

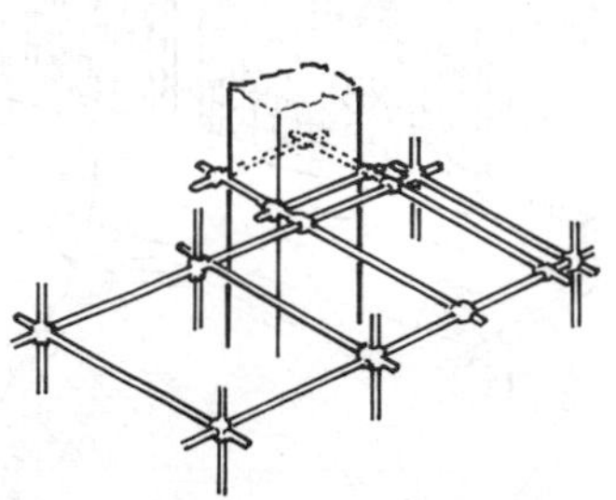

Box tie

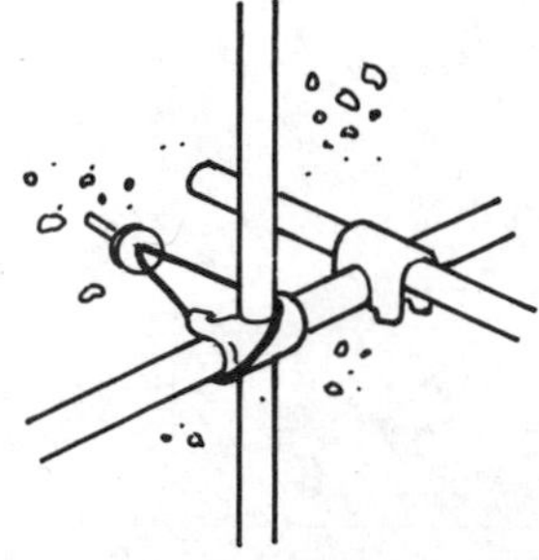

'Cast in' ring tie

Bracing can be one of two types:

Longitudinal or zig-zag bracing is fixed to the standards at an angle of approximately 45 degrees every 30 m or less. This is intended to prevent sideways movement of the scaffold.

Diagonal bracing is fixed diagonally to each alternate pair of standards at right angles to the building. They may be fixed either parallel to each other or in a zig-zag pattern. Whichever method is used, the bracing should continue the full height of the scaffold. This tends to hold the scaffold into the building.

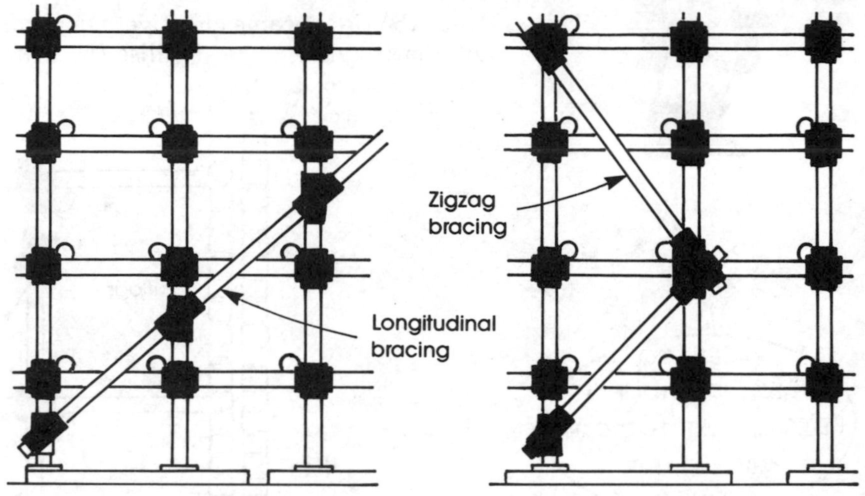

Working platform

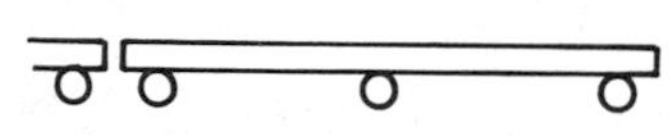

This should be four or five 38 mm × 220 mm scaffold boards in width. Each board should normally have at least three supports in order to prevent undue sagging. Where there is a danger of high winds the scaffold boards should be clipped down to putlogs or transoms. A clear passage of 440 mm (640 mm for barrows) must be maintained when loading out with materials.

Guard rails

These must be fitted to all working platforms where it is possible for a person or materials to fall 2 m or more. Fixed to the inside of the standards

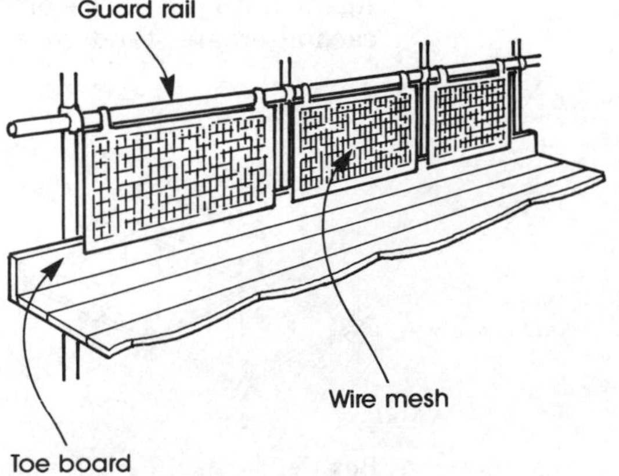

along the outside edge and the ends of the working platform, they are also required on the inside of the scaffold in the following circumstances:

- where the gap between the scaffold and the inside of an existing building exceeds 300 mm
- where the scaffold rises above a building
- where recesses occur in the building.

Guard rails must be between 910 mm and 1150 mm above the platform and not more than 765 mm above the top of the toe board.

Where materials are stacked on a scaffold the use of steel wire mesh panels is recommended.

Toe boards – accompany the guard rail and must rise at least 150 mm above the working platform. They prevent items being kicked or falling off.

Learning task

Identify the following scaffold fittings:

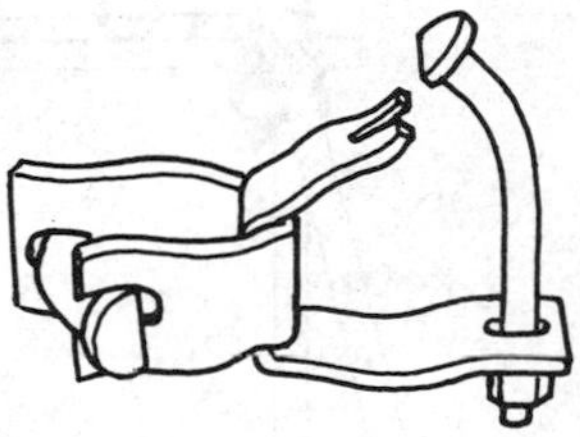

1 ....

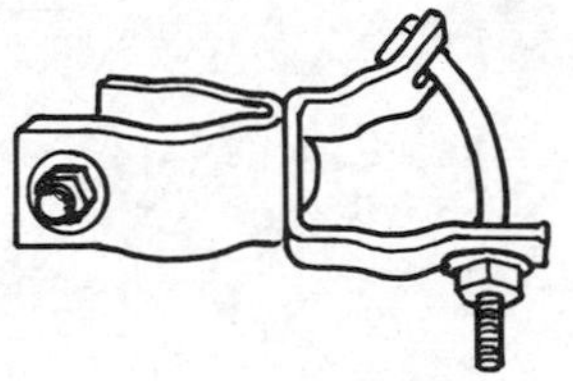

2 ....

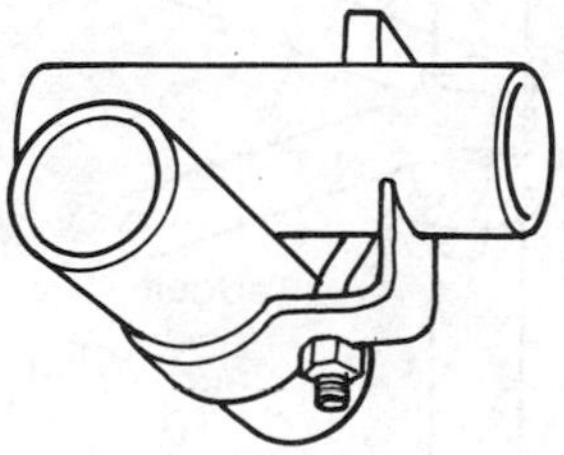

3 ....

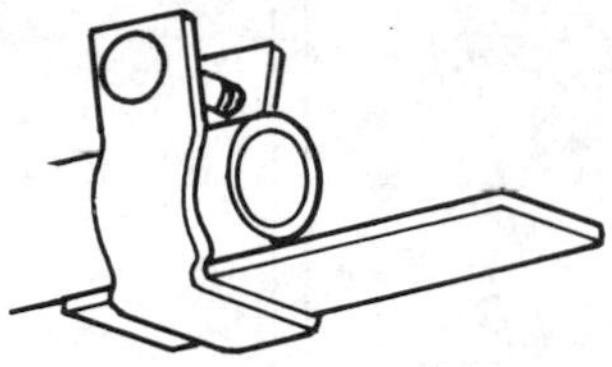

4 ....

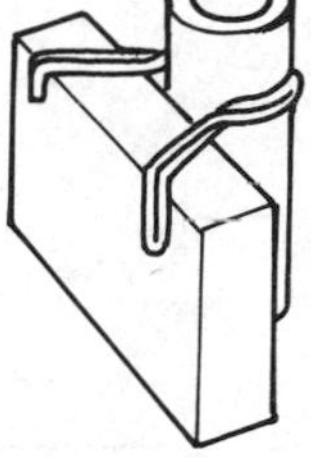

5 ....

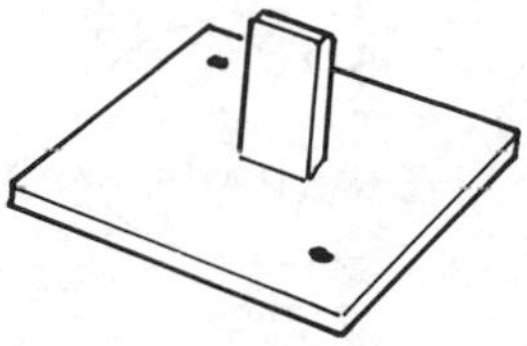

6 ....

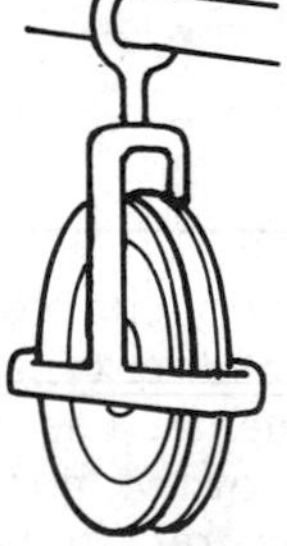

7 ....

8 ....

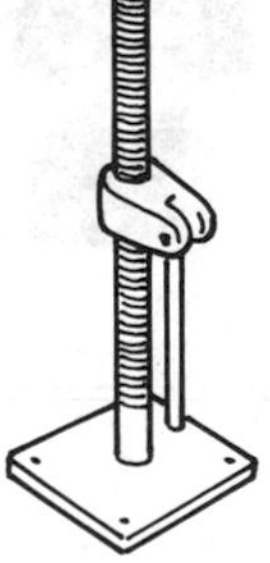

9 ....

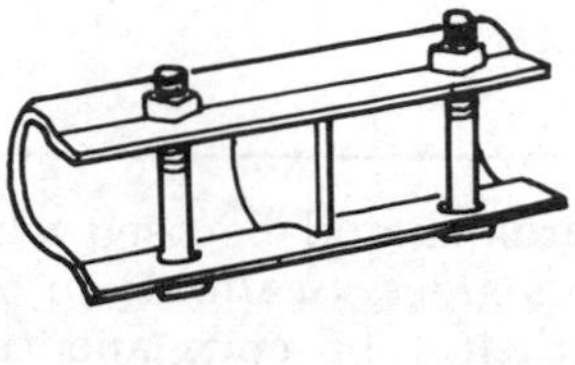

10 ....

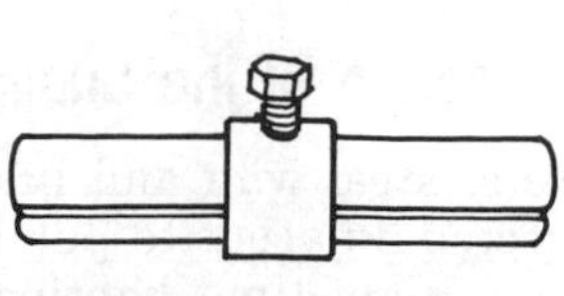

11 ....

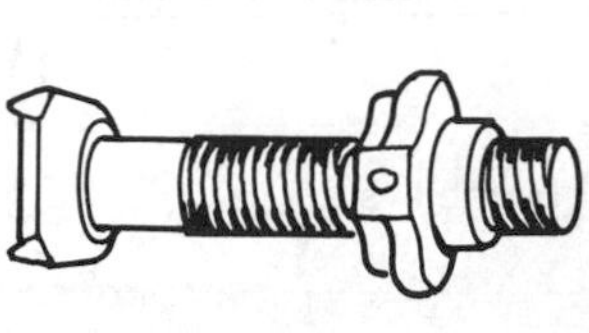

12 ....

Ladder access

The ladder should be set at a working angle of 75 degrees. This is a slope of four units vertical to one unit horizontal. The stiles of the ladder should stand on a firm base and be securely held at the top and bottom to prevent sideways or outward movement. The top of the ladder must rise at least 1.05 m (five rungs) above the landing point, unless other adequate handhold is provided. Where ladders are required to rise more than 9 m, a properly guarded intermediate landing stage must be provided.

Ladders should be boarded over to prevent access after working hours.

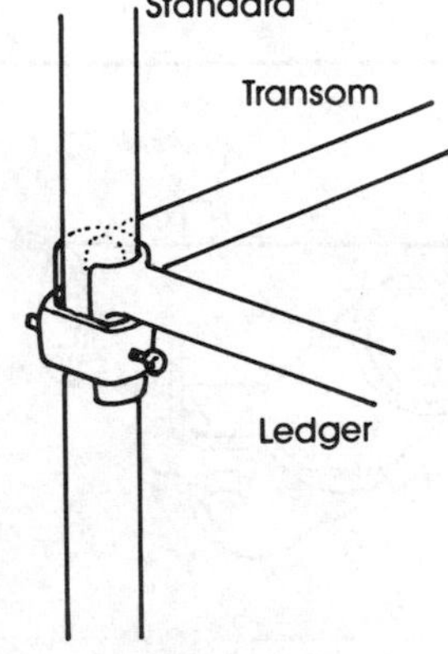

'Interlock' system

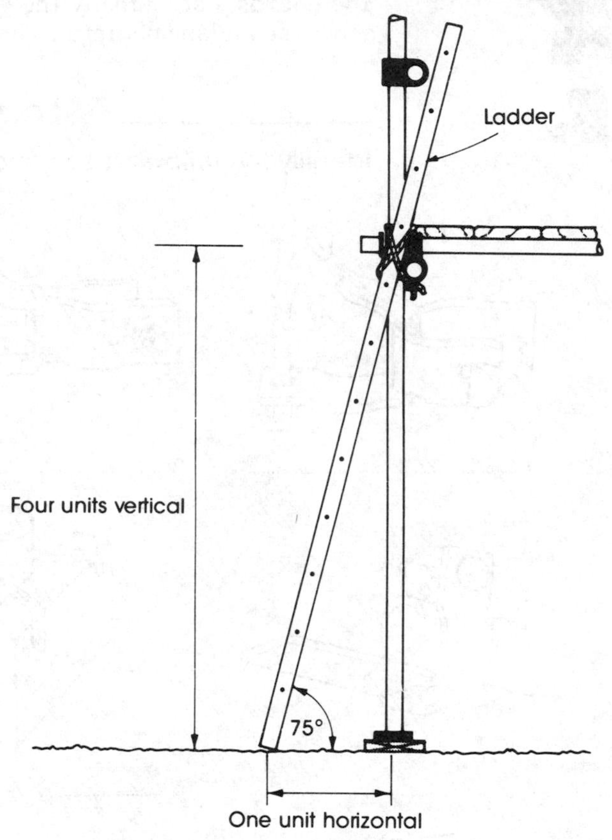

Proprietary scaffolds

These are prefabricated and require very simple erection procedures on site. They are either an independent or tower type, consisting of a range of interlocking or no-bolt jointed components. These are made to individual manufacturers' 'systems' and parts cannot normally be interchanged. Reference should be made to manufacturers' publications for this type of scaffold.

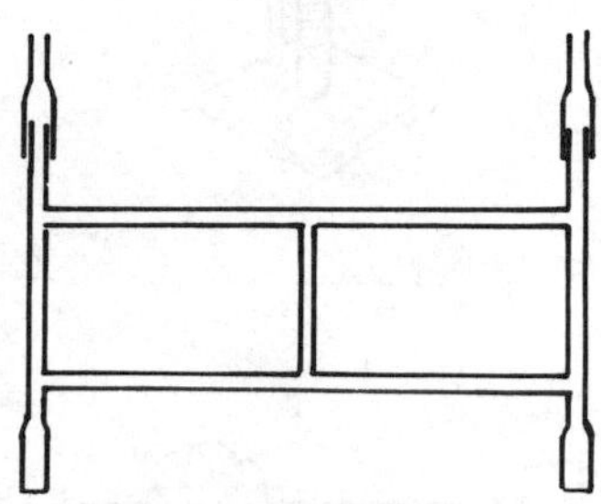

'H' frame system

Protection of the public

Nets, steel wire and brick guards should be used where scaffolds are erected adjacent to public access areas. Scaffolds on pavements should have night-time lighting and their tube ends and threads should be protected with a soft material to prevent a contact injury.

Inspection

Each scaffold must be inspected by an experienced, competent person. This is normally the responsibility of the site safety supervisor and the inspection should be carried out as follows:

- after erection, before the scaffold is used and at least once every seven days
- after cold weather, heavy rainfall or high winds.

Each inspection must be recorded in a scaffold register which is kept on site. The safety supervisor should be looking at all of the different points to ensure that the scaffold complies with the regulations.

READ THE INSTRUCTIONS AND COMPLETE THE TASK

Learning task

Carry out a safety inspection of a scaffold on your site or training establishment using this form:

Factories Act 1961

Construction (Working Places) Regulations 1966

SECTION A

Name or title of employer or contractor ______________

Address of site ______________

Work commenced—Date ______________

SCAFFOLD INSPECTIONS

Reports of results of inspections under Regulations 22 of scaffolds, including boatswain's chairs, cages, skips and similar plant or equipment (and plant or equipment used for the purposes thereof)

Location and description of scaffold, etc. and other plant or equipment inspected (1)	Date of inspection (2)	Result of inspection State whether in good order (3)	Signature (or, in case where signature is not legally required, name) of person who made the inspection (4)

NOTES TO SECTION A

(1) *Short check list – at each inspection check that your scaffolding does not have these faults:*

		Week 1	2	3	4
FOOTINGS	Soft and uneven, No base plates, No sole boards, Undermined				
STANDARDS	Not plumb, Joined at same height, Wrong spacing, Damaged				
LEDGERS	Not level, Joint in same bays, Loose, Damaged				

		Week 1	2	3	4
BRACING 'Facade and ledger'	Some missing, Loose, Wrong fittings				
PUTLOGS and TRANSOMS	Wrongly spaced, Loose, Wrongly supported				
COUPLINGS	Wrong fitting, Loose, Damaged, No check couplers				
BRIDLES	Wrong spacing, Wrong couplings, Weak support				

		Week 1	2	3	4
TIES	Some missing, Loose				
BOARDING	Bad boards, Trap boards, Incomplete, Insufficient supports				
GUARD RAILS & TOE BOARDS	Wrong height, Loose, Some missing				
LADDERS	Damaged, Insufficient length, Not tied				

(2) *This check list is not part of the report required by Regulation 22: see also para 5 of Notes and Regulation 22 on page (ii) of cover and Notes on page 13.*

HOW'S IT GOING?

Other working platforms

Hop-up working platforms

These are purpose-made by craft operatives, normally from softwood boarding or plywood. They should be at least 400 mm wide, about 500 mm high and have two steps. The top should be at least 500 mm square when used as a working platform.

Single hop-ups provide an isolated working platform, whereas two hop-ups spanned by boards enable a much greater area to be covered.

Hop-ups are intended to provide a working platform for reasonably low surfaces, up to about 2.4 m, without too much stretching.

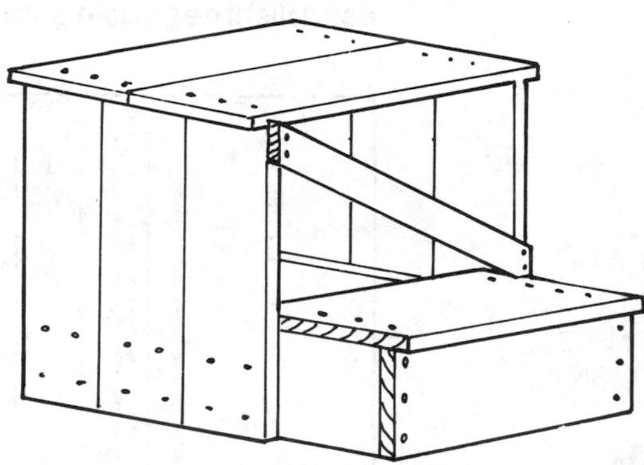

Split-head type working platforms

These utilise tripod-type adjustable metal split heads in conjunction with timber joists and scaffold boards. A series of holes and pin or screw jacks adjusts the working platform's height. These must be cleaned after use to ensure ease of working.

Four split heads are required to support the smallest working platform, eight or more split heads can be combined to board out larger areas.

These structures are intended to provide a working platform for work on ceilings.

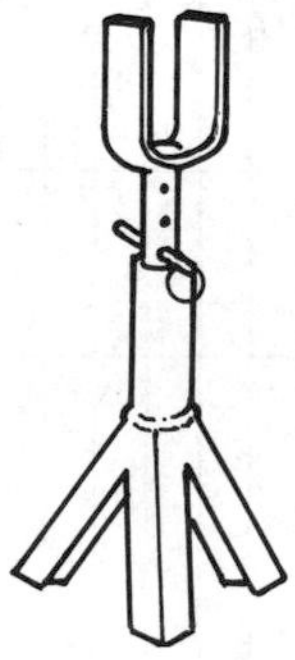

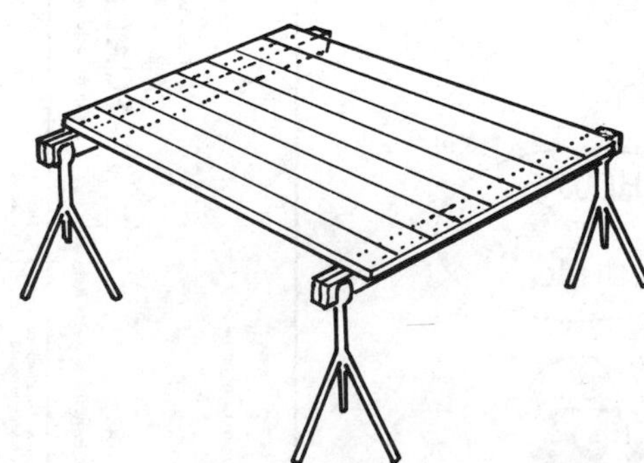

Staging boards

These are proprietary items used in conjunction with hop-ups, split heads, steps or trestles, to enable longer spans between supports. They are

manufactured in timber with metal tie rods and reinforcing wires and are available in a variety of lengths from 1.8 m to about 7 m and at a standard width of 450 mm and are suitable for supporting up to three persons. Consult the manufacturers' information for specific details.

Staging boards must not be used if they have any broken, damaged, repaired or missing parts. In addition they should not be painted, as this may hide defects. On finding defects the item must be taken out of use immediately, labelled as defective with 'DO NOT USE', and reported as soon as possible to your chargehand/foreman.

In use, staging boards must overhang their support by at least 50 mm but not by more than four times their thickness.

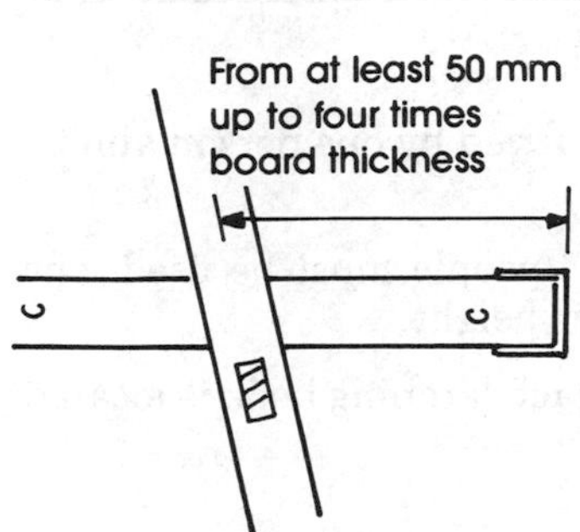

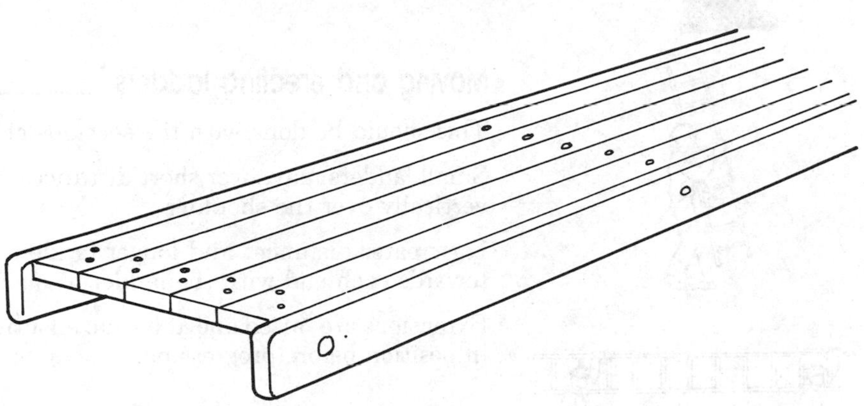

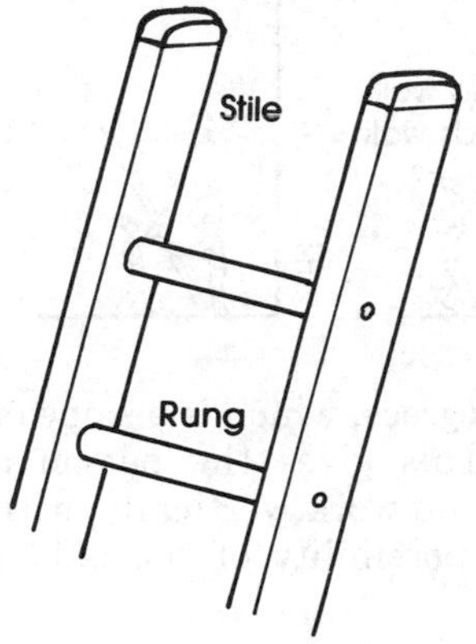

Ladders

These are used to enable access to higher level working platforms or to provide a very short-term position for light work (painting) at heights. They may be either timber or aluminium and they consist of two long stiles which support rungs at about 250 mm centres.

Single-section ladders, termed standing ladders, can be obtained up to around 7 m in length.

Multi-section ladders, termed extension ladders (double or triple according to the number of sections), are fitted with latching hooks to the bottom of the extension section(s) and guide brackets to the top of the lower section(s). The latching hooks locate over the rung of the section below when extended and the guide brackets keep the sections together. Lengths of extension ladders vary from about 3 to 7 m when closed, extending up to approximately 19 m.

The extending section may be rope-operated to facilitate erection.

Aluminium ladders are often fitted with ladder feet. These are patent non-slip devices such as serrated rubber blocks or suction pads.

Aluminium ladders are often preferred to timber ladders. They are lighter, stronger, rot-proof and in addition will not warp, twist or burn, but do not use them near overhead electric cables.

Timber pole ladders are used mainly for scaffold access.

Timber standing ladders are made from Douglas fir, redwood, whitewood or hemlock. Rungs are round or rectangular. Steel tie rods should be fitted at intervals of not more than nine rungs apart and also under the second rung from each end of the ladder. Stiles may be reinforced by wires housed and clipped to their undersides.

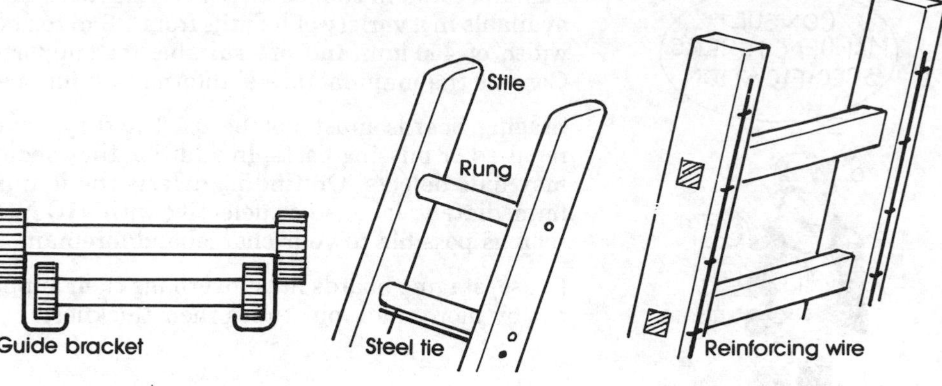

Moving and erecting ladders

This should be done with the sections closed.

Small ladders may, over short distances, be carried by one person almost vertically over the shoulder.

For greater distances and longer ladders, two people must be used, one towards each end with the ladder at shoulder height.

Extensions are raised one at a time ensuring each latching hook is located in position before progressing.

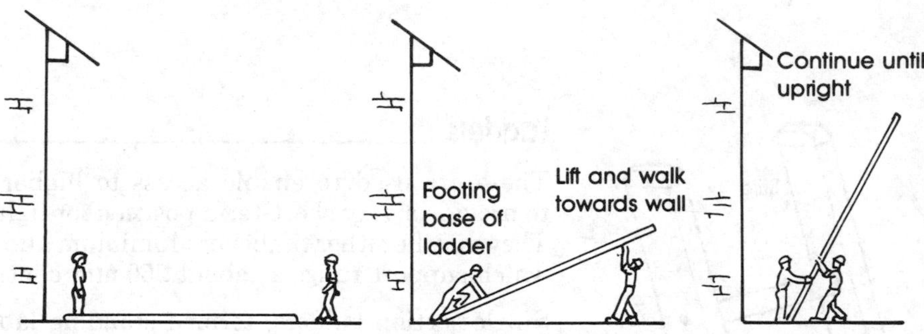

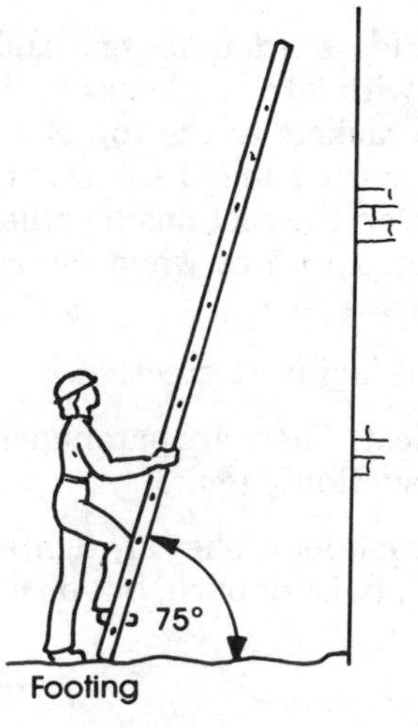

When erected the working angle should be 75 degrees, which is a slope of four vertical units to one horizontal unit. This gives the person a comfortable angle at which to ascend, descend and work, vertically, with arms extended. In addition it minimises the possibility of the ladder slipping outwards from the base.

Ladders must be of sufficient length for the work in hand, sited on a firm, level base. They must be securely fixed by tying at the top or where this is not possible either by the stake and guy rope method or by having someone foot the ladder. (The footer must pay attention to the work in hand at all times and not 'watch the scenery'.) This is to prevent the ladder from slipping outwards from the base and the top sliding sideways.

Never over-reach when working on a ladder. Always take the time to stop and move it.

Sections of extension ladders must overlap sufficiently for strength. This is normally at least two rungs for short ladders and up to four rungs for longer ones. Consult manufacturers' recommendations for specific details.

Ladders should be lowered at the end of the working day and locked away. Where this is not practical, the lower rungs should be securely covered with a tied scaffold board to prevent public access. Always store flat to prevent twisting.

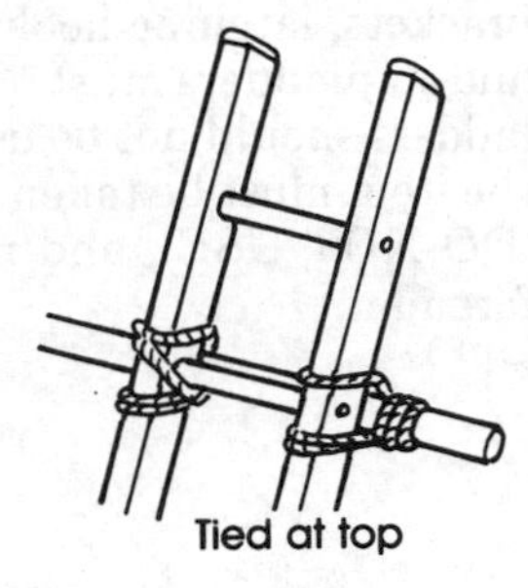

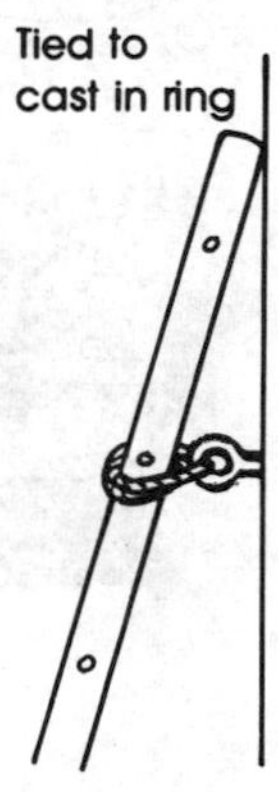

Stepladders

These are used mainly internally on firm flat surfaces and must be fully opened. They provide a working platform where the work area is just out of reach. Like ladders, they may be timber or aluminium, consisting of stiles supporting flat treads at about 250 mm centres. A back frame hinged at the top and secured towards the bottom with a cord or locking bar ensures the correct working angle and checks the opening to prevent collapse.

Stepladders are available in a range of tread lengths, commonly from five to fourteen.

They must be used at right angles to the workface whenever possible (this reduces risk of sideways overturning). The user's knees should be below the top step.

They may be used in pairs in conjunction with boarding to provide a longer working platform, in which case the board must overhang the treads by at least 50 mm but by not more than four times the board's thickness.

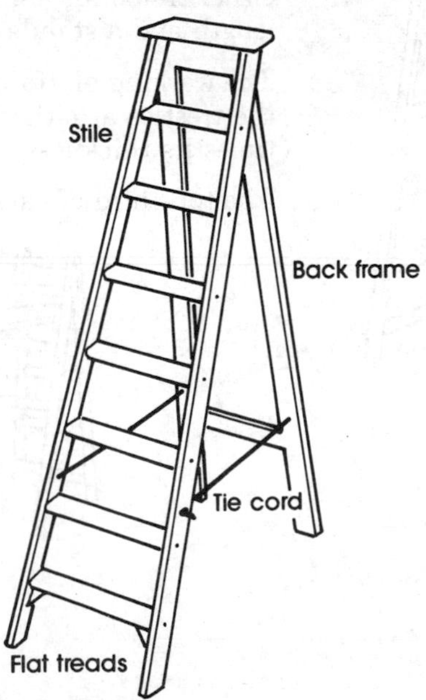

Aluminium stepladders are often preferred to timber ladders; they are lighter, stronger, rot-proof and in addition will not warp, twist or burn.

Ladders and stepladders must not be used if they have any broken, damaged, repaired or missing parts. Check particularly ropes, guide brackets, latching hooks, locking bars and pulley wheels. Timber ladders and stepladders must not be painted as this may hide defects. Aluminium ladders should not be used near overhead power lines. On finding defects the item must be taken out of use immediately, labelled as defective with 'DO NOT USE', and reported as soon as possible to your chargehand/foreman.

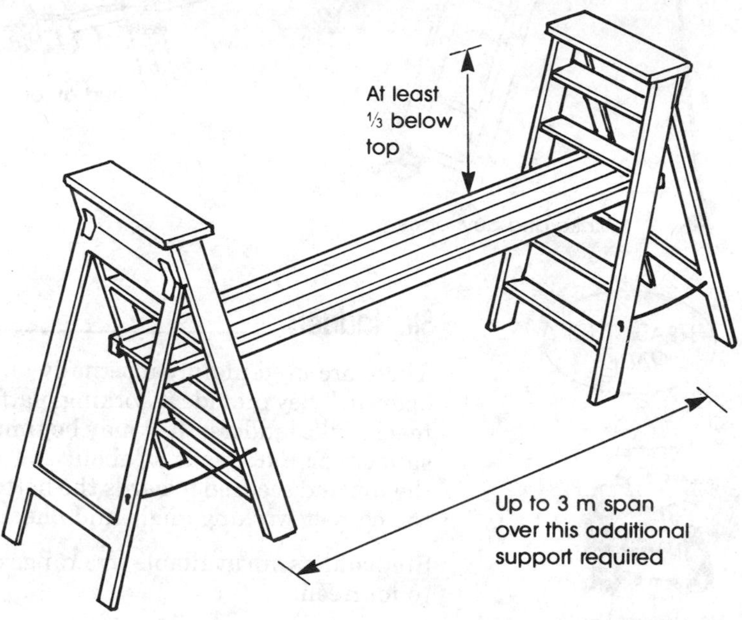

Trestle scaffolds

These are used mainly internally on firm, flat surfaces and must be fully opened. They provide a working platform for light work (painting etc.), where the working platform is up to 4.5 m in height.

They are used in pairs in conjunction with boarding and are available in either timber or aluminium and in a variety of sizes up to about 7 m in length and a standard width of 450 mm.

The working platform must be at least 430 mm wide and must overhang the trestles at either end by at least 50 mm, but by not more than four times its thickness.

The top third of each trestle must be above the working platform.

Working platforms over 2 m high will require a separate pair of steps or ladder for access and those over 3.6 m should be securely tied to the building or other suitable anchorage for stability.

It is recommended that work is carried out in the sitting position when the platform is above about 1.8 m.

Folding trestle platforms do not require guardrails or toe boards but fixed trestle platforms do, where a person may fall more than 2 m.

Trestles must not be used if they have any broken, damaged, repaired or missing parts. Timber trestles must not be painted as this may hide defects. Aluminium trestles should not be used near overhead power lines. On finding defects the item must be taken out of use immediately, labelled as defective with 'DO NOT USE', and reported as soon as possible to your chargehand/foreman.

Working safety

All scaffolding and working platforms must be clean, in good order and checked by a competent person before use and periodically after erection.

For your own safety

- Carry out a check yourself prior to use.
- Do not use if unsafe; consult chargehand/supervisor for approval.
- Report any defects to your chargehand/foreman.
- Do not remove any part from a scaffold or working platform. *You* may be responsible for its total collapse.
- Do not use a working platform in adverse weather conditions, high winds, heavy rain, snow or ice, etc.
- Do not block the working platform. Ensure a free passage for other people.
- Clear up your 'mess' as you go and also before leaving the working platform.
- Do not push your mess over the edge. Ensure it is properly lowered.

Questions for you

1. State the reason for **not** painting timber scaffold equipment.

TRY AND ANSWER THESE

2. State the purpose of:
(a) a toe board (b) a guardrail

3. Name two parts of a ladder or stepladder.

4. Ladders should be fixed to the scaffold at a working angle of:
(a) 60 degrees
(b) 45 degrees
(c) 90 degrees
(d) 75 degrees

a	b	c	d
[ ]	[ ]	[ ]	[ ]

5. Why does a putlog have a flattened end?

6. State the purpose of longitudinal bracing.

7. State the procedure to be adopted on finding a pair of stepladders with a defective tread.

8. State **TWO** methods which may be used to secure ladders.

9. Explain why materials stacked on a scaffold should be kept to a minimum.

WORD-SQUARE SEARCH

Hidden in the word-square are the following 20 words associated with '*Scaffolding*'. You may find the words written forwards, backwards, up, down or diagonally.

Scaffold	Ledgers
Putlog	Bracing
Ladder	Transom
Trestle	Toe board
Hop up	Couplers
Split heads	Sole plates
Regulations	Tower
Independent	Platform
Board	Proprietary
Standards	Guard rail

Draw a ring around the words, or line in using a highlight pen thus:

EXAMPLE

EXAMPLE

P	L	A	T	F	O	R	M	S	S	D	L	O	F	F	A	C	S
R	U	S	P	L	I	T	H	E	A	D	S	R	R	E	W	O	T
O	R	T	S	L	L	M	F	D	N	D	H	O	P	U	P	P	A
P	I	C	L	A	D	D	E	R	L	S	P	M	B	M	E	O	N
R	A	D	D	O	Y	A	N	E	T	E	C	O	O	U	H	R	D
I	U	H	L	N	G	O	T	G	G	T	C	S	L	N	E	T	A
E	A	N	O	E	P	A	K	U	O	A	D	N	A	I	L	T	R
T	L	W	V	P	E	S	S	L	G	L	S	A	H	C	M	N	D
A	I	T	O	S	U	S	Y	A	I	P	O	R	T	A	E	E	S
R	A	C	O	C	C	P	R	T	R	E	S	T	L	E	T	D	N
Y	R	O	R	I	H	O	G	I	A	L	H	O	C	I	S	N	I
U	D	N	E	L	E	G	T	O	S	O	A	E	A	O	T	E	W
R	R	S	P	V	N	D	A	N	C	S	D	B	N	N	P	P	A
O	A	T	V	I	U	S	T	S	M	E	R	O	I	C	C	E	R
L	U	R	C	O	U	P	L	E	R	S	I	A	T	I	O	D	D
K	G	A	T	I	E	L	E	T	T	E	R	R	O	D	C	N	V
F	R	C	T	A	S	B	M	L	A	D	E	D	E	R	S	I	E
B	S	P	B	O	A	R	D	C	A	T	S	R	E	G	D	E	L

5 Materials

On-site provision for storage of materials

Site storage provision

A building site can be seen as a temporary factory, a workshop and materials store from which a contractor will construct a building.

An important consideration when planning the layout of this temporary factory is the storage of materials.

Their positioning should be planned in relation to where on site they are to be used, whilst at the same time providing protection and security.

Large valuable items

Frames, pipes and drainage fittings, etc. should be stored in a lockable, fully fenced compound.

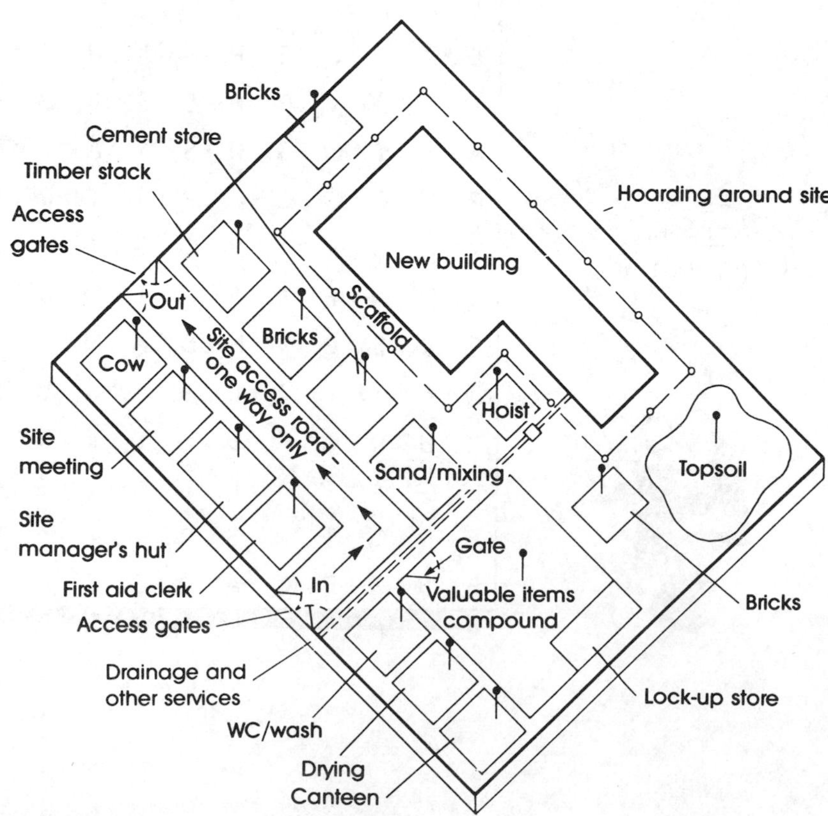

Smaller valuable items

Carpenters' ironmongery, fixings; plumbers' copper pipe, fittings, appliances; electricians' wire, fittings; and paint, should be kept secure in one or more lockable site huts, this will depend on the size of the site. Like items should be stored adjacent to each other on shelving or in a bin system, as appropriate.

Each shelf or bin should be clearly marked with its contents, and each item entered on a tally card.

If materials are returned to stock they should be put back in the correct place and the tally card amended.

Heavy items should be stored at low level.

New deliveries should be put at the back of existing stock. This ensures stock is used in rotation and does not deteriorate due to an exceeded shelf-life, making it useless.

BBS SUPPLIERS TALLY CARD

Description of materials: WHITE GLOSS Ref No: BSB 14/2

Size or No: 5 LITRE

Date	Order No.	Amount Inwards	Amount Outwards	Signature	Balance
15·3·90	B14	50		PB	50
18·3·90			10	PB	40
27·3·90			12	PB	28
19·4·90	B75	30		PB	58
20·4·90			16	PB	42

Issues of stores should be undertaken by a storeperson or supervisor against an authorised requisition. Each issue should be recorded on the tally card. On some sites the tally card system of recording the issue of materials may have been superseded by the use of a computerised system.

BBS SUPPLIES
DELIVERY NOTE

Registered office

No. 498/PSB/1

Date 30-4-90

Delivered to
BBS SITE STORE
BROOKLYN
GREAT BARR B41

Invoice to
HEAD OFFICE

Please receive in good condition the undermentioned goods

10 OFF 5L WHITE GLOSS
25 OFF 10L WHITE UNDERCOAT
10 OFF DUST SHEETS
10 OFF 1L FINE SURFACE FILLER
10 OFF 2.5 L WHITE SPIRIT
10 OFF 2.5L RED GLOSS

Received by BB
Remarks
Note Claims for sh

BBS SITE REQUISITION

Job No.	Item	Description	Amount	Remarks
4/1	WHITE UNDERCOAT		50L	
4/1	WHITE GLOSS		25L	
4/1	FINE SURFACE FILLER		2L	
4/1	M2 GLASS PAPER		10 SHEETS	
4/1	WHITE SPIRIT		7.5L	

Date: 2.5.90
Person receiving: .... Authorised by: J. PHIPPS J Phipps
Person issuing: ....

HOW'S IT GOING?

Learning task

Update the following tally cards to include these latest deliveries and the site requisition information. (See page 128.)

BBS SUPPLIERS TALLY CARD

Description of materials: WHITE UNDERCOAT   Ref No: BSB 15/3

Size or No: 10 LITRE

Date	Order No.	Amount Inwards	Amount Outwards	Signature	Balance
8.3.90	B11	65		BB	65
15.3.90			10	BB	55
16.3.90			1	BB	54
18.3.90			15	BB	39
27.4.90			12	BB	27

BBS SUPPLIERS TALLY CARD

Description of materials: WHITE SPIRIT   Ref No: BSB 15/50

Size or No: 2.5 LITRE

Date	Order No.	Amount Inwards	Amount Outwards	Signature	Balance
8.3.90	B12	10		BB	10
18.3.90			2	BB	8
27.3.90			3	BB	5
30.3.90	B54	10		BB	15
20.4.90			4	BB	11
28.4.90			3	BB	8

Storage requirements

Different materials have different storage requirements. Points to bear in mind are:

Delivery dates – phased deliveries of material should be considered in line with the planned construction programme. This will prevent unnecessarily long periods of site storage and unnecessarily large storage areas being needed.

Physical size, weight and delivery method – will determine what plant (crane or fork-lift truck, etc.) and labour is required for off-loading and stacking.

Protection – many materials are destroyed by extremes of temperature, absorption of moisture, or exposure to sunlight, etc.

Stores should be maintained as far as possible at an even temperature of about 15 °C.

High temperatures cause adhesives, paints, varnishes, putties and mastics, etc. to dry out and harden.

Flammable liquids such as white spirit, thinner, paraffin, petrol, some paints and varnishes, some timber preservatives and some formwork release agents must be stored in a cool, dry, lockable place. Fumes from such liquids present a fire hazard and can have an overpowering effect if inhaled. Stores of this type should always have two or more fire exits and be equipped with suitable fire extinguishers in case of fire. (See 'Health and Safety'.)

Water-based materials, such as emulsion paints and formwork release agents, may be ruined if allowed to freeze.

Non-durable materials such as timber, cement and plaster require weather protection to prevent moisture absorption.

Boxed or canned dry materials, such as powder adhesives, wallpaper paste, fillers, detergent powders and sugar soap quickly become useless if exposed to any form of dampness. Dampness will also rust metal containers which may result in leakage and contamination of the contents.

Where materials are stored in a building under construction, ensure the building:

- has dried out after so-called 'wet trades', such as brickwork and plastering, are finished
- is fully glazed and preferably heated
- is well ventilated – this is essential to prevent the build-up of high humidity (warm moist air).

Transit Non-durable materials should be delivered in closed or tarpaulin-covered lorries. This will protect them from both wet weather and moisture absorption from damp or humid atmospheres.

Handling Careless or unnecessary repeated handling will result in increased costs through damaged materials and even personal injury.

Security Many building materials are 'desirable' items, they will 'grow legs' and walk away if site security lapses.

Safety Finally, take care of your personal hygiene. This is just as important as any physical protection measure. Certain building materials, e.g. cement, admixtures and release agents, can have an irritant effect on skin contact; they are poisonous if swallowed and can result in narcosis if their vapour or powder is inhaled. By taking proper precautions these harmful effects can be avoided. Follow manufacturers' instructions; avoid inhaling spray mists, fumes and powders; wear disposable gloves or a barrier cream; thoroughly wash hands before eating, drinking, smoking, and after work. In case of accidental inhalation, swallowing or contact with skin, eyes, etc. medical advice should be sought immediately.

Caution, risk of fire

Caution, toxic hazard

Caution, corrosive substance

Take note of material labelling and manufacturers' instructions

Questions for you

TRY AND ANSWER THESE

1. State the purpose of storing materials on site.

WELL, HOW DID YOU DO?

2. Briefly describe **THREE** main points to be considered when determining on-site storage requirements.

WORK THROUGH THE SECTION AGAIN IF YOU HAD ANY PROBLEMS

Storage of bulk durable building materials

Bricks

These are walling unit components having a standard size, including a 10 mm mortar allowance, of 225 mm × 112.5 mm × 75 mm.

Bricks are normally made from either calcium silicate or clay. Clay bricks are usually pressed, cut or moulded and then fired in a kiln at very high temperatures. Their density, strength, colour and surface texture will depend on the variety of clay used and the firing temperature. Calcium silicate bricks are pressed into shape and steamed at high temperature. Pigments may be added during the manufacturing process to achieve a range of colours.

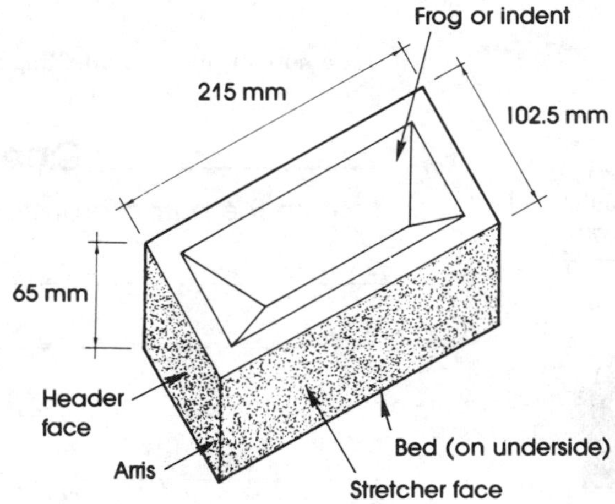

Pressed
(Regular in shape with sharp edges)

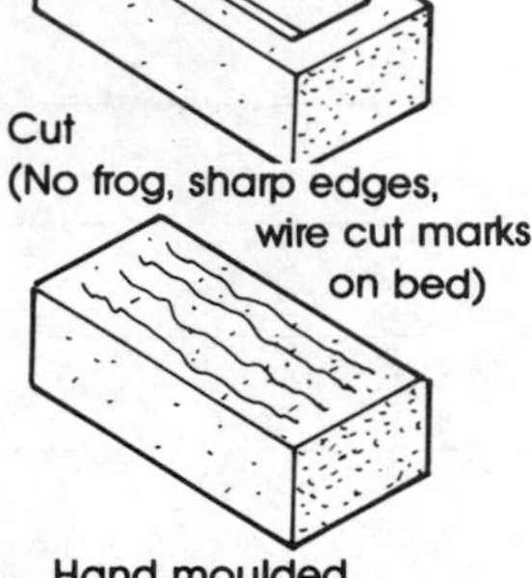

Cut
(No frog, sharp edges, wire cut marks on bed)

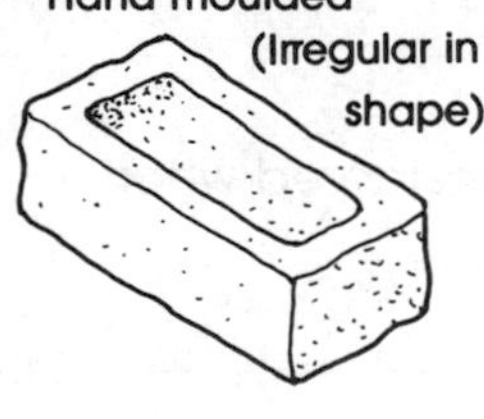

Hand moulded
(Irregular in shape)

The three main types of bricks are as follows:

Common or fletton bricks are basic bricks used in the main for internal or covered (rendered or cladded) external work, although sand-faced flettons are available for use as cheap facing bricks.

Facing bricks are made from selected clays and are chosen for their attractive appearance rather than any other performance characteristic.

Engineering bricks have a very high density and strength and do not absorb moisture; they are used in both highly loaded and damp conditions such as inspection chambers, basements and other sub-structure work.

Bricks may be supplied loose or banded in unit loads, shrink-wrapped in plastic and sometimes on timber pallets.

Loose bricks should be off-loaded manually, never tipped; they should be stacked on edge in rows, on level, well-drained ground. Do not stack too high: up to a maximum of 1.8 m.

Careless handling, can chip the faces and arrises (corners), and also lead to fractures, making the bricks useless for both face and hidden work. Poor stacking creates an untidy workplace and unsafe conditions for those working or passing through the area.

Banded loads of up to 500 are off-loaded mechanically using either the lorry-mounted device, a fork-lift truck or a crane. Bricks stacked on polythene or timber pallets will be protected from the absorption of sulphates and other contaminants which could later mar the finished brickwork.

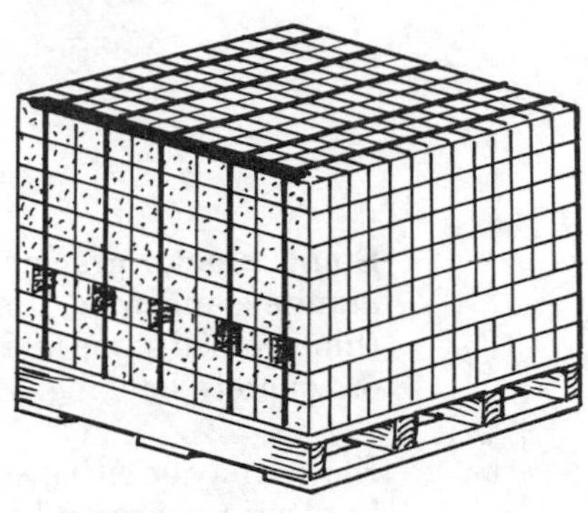

To protect bricks against rain, frost and atmospheric pollution, all stacks should be covered with a tarpaulin or polythene sheets weighted at the bottom.

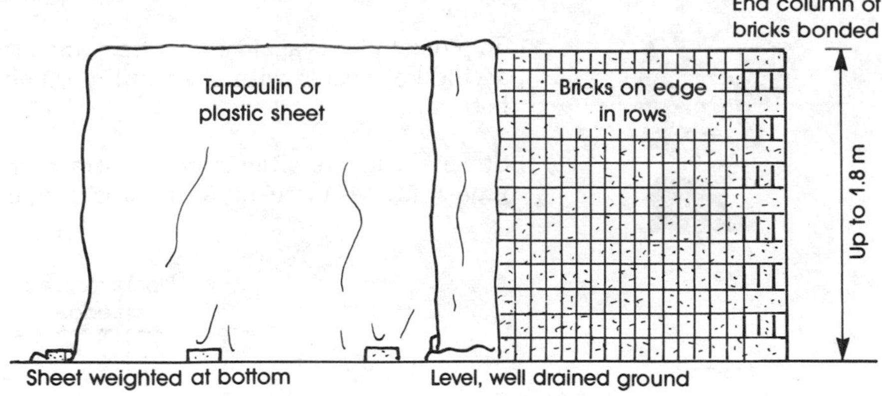

Blocks

These are walling units which are larger than bricks, normally made either from concrete or natural stone.

Concrete blocks can be either dense or lightweight; dense blocks are often made hollow to lighten them, lightweight blocks can use either a lightweight aggregate or a fine aggregate that is aerated to form air bubbles. Concrete blocks are most often used for internal partition walls or the inner leaf of cavity walls. When used externally, they are normally either rendered (covered with a thin layer of cement mortar) or covered in cladding (tiles, slates or timber), to provide a waterproof construction. The main advantage of blocks over bricks is their increased speed of laying and also the good thermal insulation qualities of the aerated variety.

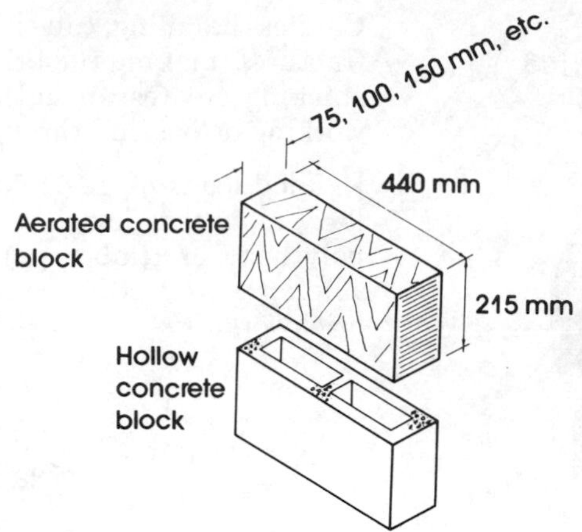

Stone blocks are made from a naturally occurring material such as granite, sandstone, limestone, marble and slate. They are mainly used as thin-dressed stone facings known as ashlar, which are fixed to a brickwork or concrete backing.

Blocks may be either supplied loose, banded in unit loads, shrink-wrapped in plastic packs and sometimes on timber pallets.

Loose blocks should be off-loaded manually, never tipped; they should be stacked on edge in rows or columns, on level, well drained ground. Do not stack too high: six to eight courses maximum.

Banded or palleted loads are off-loaded mechanically using either the lorry-mounted device, a fork-lift truck or a crane.

To protect blocks against rain, frost and atmospheric pollution, all stacks should be covered with a tarpaulin or polythene sheets weighted at the bottom.

Stone blocks are often stored in straw, or other similar soft packing to protect arrises (corners) from impact damage.

STUDY THESE DIAGRAMS

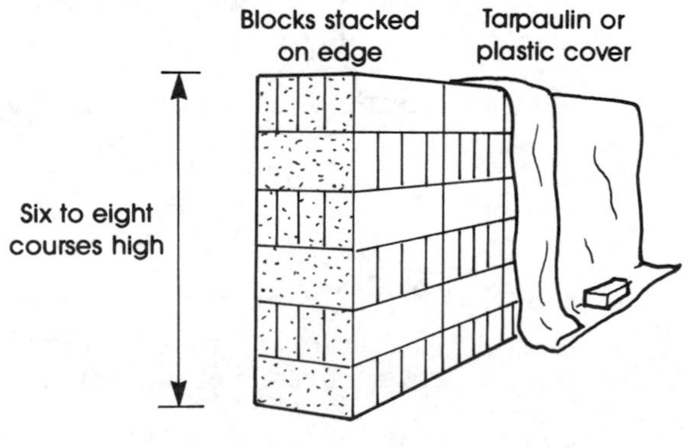

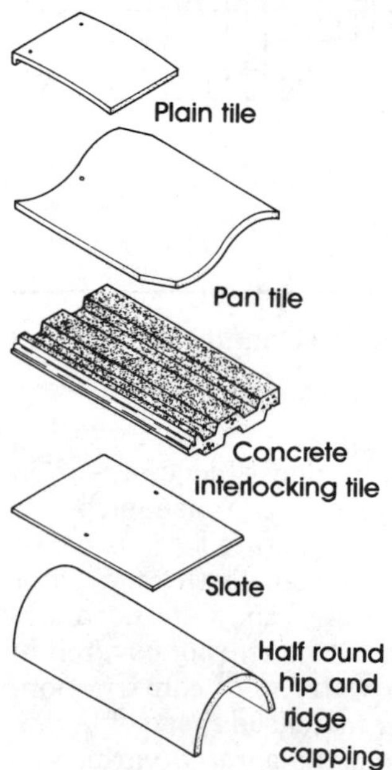

Roof tiles

These are normally either a terracotta clay product, a natural, metamorphic stone slate, or a cast concrete product.

Roof tiles may be either supplied loose, in banded packs, in shrink-wrapped plastic packs or in unit loads on timber pallets.

Loose tiles should be off-loaded manually, never tipped; they should be stacked on edge in rows, on level, well-drained ground. Do not stack too high: four to six rows maximum; and taper the stack towards the top. End tiles in each course should be laid flat to prevent toppling. Ridge and hip cappings should be stored on end.

Banded, packed or palleted loads are off-loaded mechanically using either the lorry-mounted device, a fork-lift truck or a crane.

To protect tiles against rain, frost and atmospheric pollution, all stacks should be covered with a tarpaulin or polythene sheets weighted at the bottom.

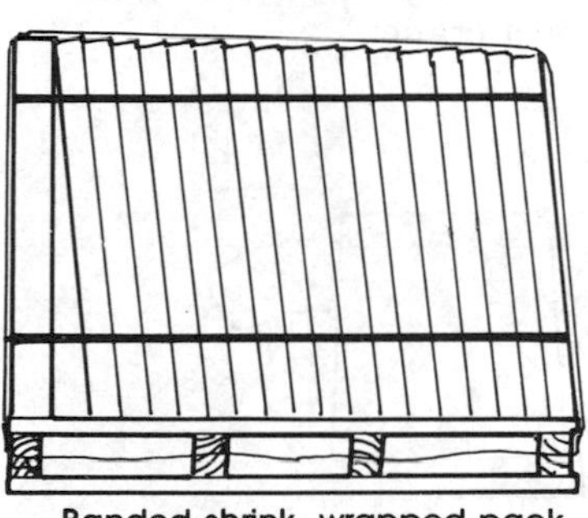

Banded shrink- wrapped pack

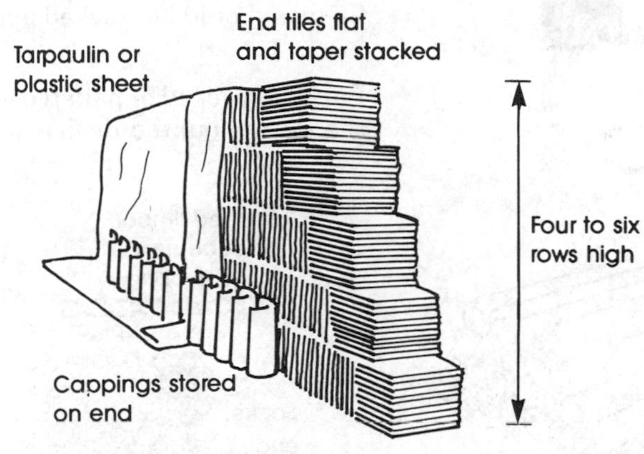

Concrete units (paving slabs, kerbs and lintels)

These are normally pre-cast in factory conditions and transported to site.

Concrete units may be either supplied loose singly, in banded packs, in shrink-wrapped plastic packs or in unit loads on timber pallets.

Loose concrete units should be off-loaded manually, never tipped. Items of equipment can be used to lift single units, e.g. kerb lifter.

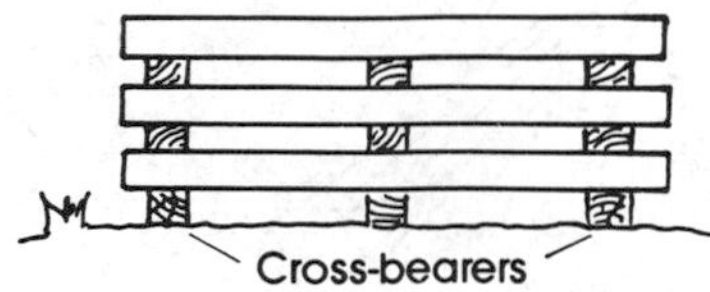

Paving slabs should be stacked on edge in single height rows, on level, well-drained ground. Intermediate stacks of slabs laid flat can be introduced to prevent toppling.

Kerbs and lintels should be stacked flat on timber cross-bearers laid on level ground. Cross-bearers should be laid between each layer, to provide a level surface, to spread the load and to prevent the risk of distortion and chipping damage. Do not stack too high: four to six layers maximum.

Lintels are designed to contain steel reinforcement towards their bottom edge, to resist tensile forces. It is most important that they are moved in the plane of intended use, otherwise they may simply fold in two. Where the steel bars or wires cannot be seen on the end, the top edge is often marked with a 'T' or 'TOP' for identification.

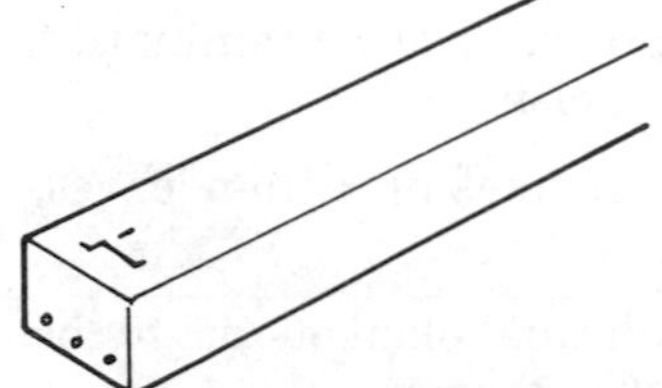

Banded, packed or palleted loads are off-loaded mechanically using either the lorry-mounted device, a fork-lift truck or a crane.

To protect concrete units against rain, frost and atmospheric pollution, they may be covered with a tarpaulin or polythene sheets weighted at the bottom.

Drainage pipes and fittings

These may be glazed or unglazed clay products, cast iron or UPVC (a rigid or unplasticised polyvinylchloride).

Drainage pipes and fittings may be either supplied loose singly, in banded packs, in shrink-wrapped plastic packs or in unit loads on timber pallets.

Loose pipes and fittings should be off-loaded manually, never tipped. Pipes should be stacked horizontally in rows and wedged or chocked to prevent rolling, on level, well-drained ground. Do not stack too high: 1.5 m maximum; and taper the stack towards the top. Spigot and socket pipes should be stacked on timber cross-bearers, alternate rows should be reversed to allow sockets to project beyond spigots. Gullies and other fittings should be stacked upside down and supported so that they remain level.

Banded, packed or palleted loads are off-loaded mechanically using either the lorry-mounted device, a fork-lift truck or a crane.

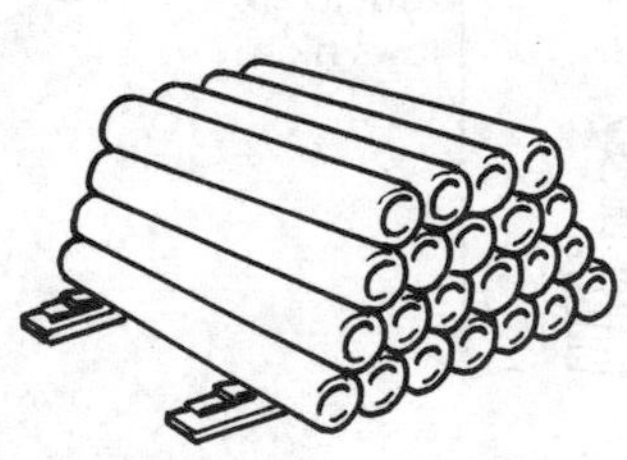

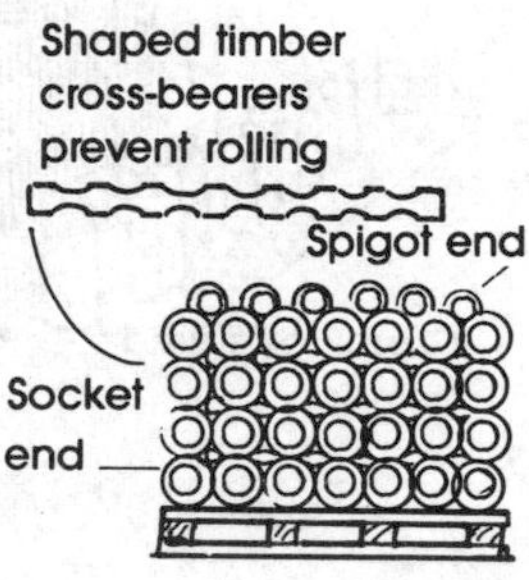

Aggregates

These are sands, gravel and crushed rock which are added to cement as a filler material to produce concrete and mortar.

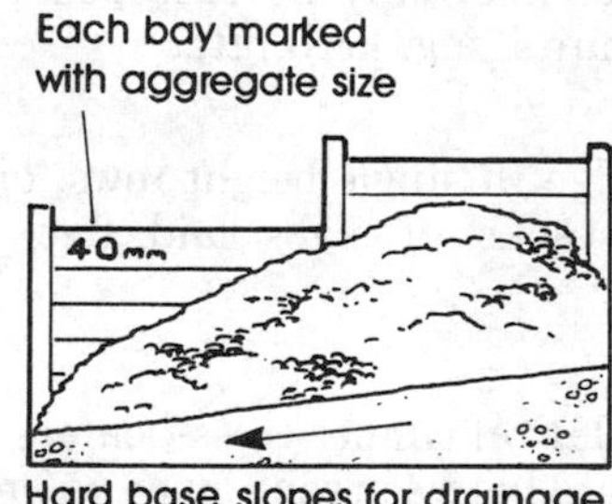

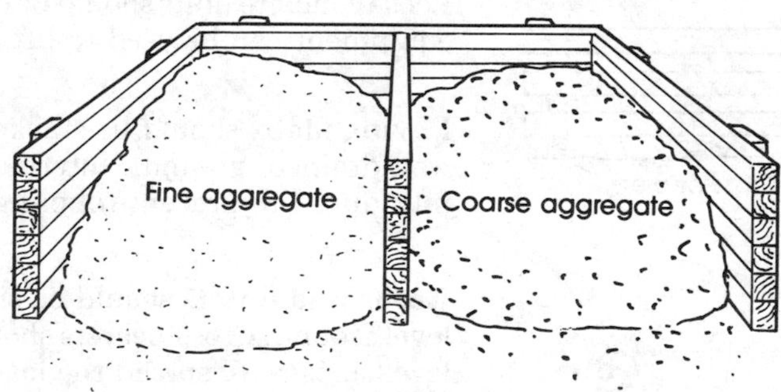

Normally supplied in bulk by tipper lorries; small amounts are available bagged. Each size should be stored separately adjacent to the mixer. Stockpiles should ideally be on a hard, concrete base, laid so that water will drain away, and separated into bays by division walls.

Stock piles should be sited away from trees to prevent leaf contamination and kept free from general site and canteen rubbish.

Tarpaulins or plastic covers can be used to protect stock piles from leaves, rubbish and rainwater.

In severe winter conditions the use of insulating blankets is to be recommended, to provide protection from frost and snow.

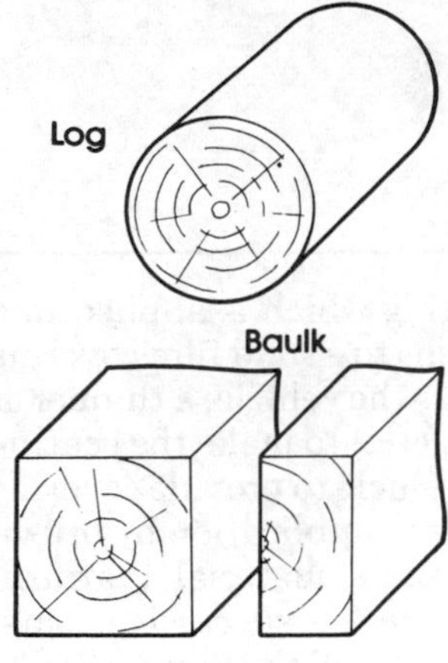

Timber

This is sawn or planed wood in its natural state – softwoods from coniferous trees and hardwoods from broadleaf trees. In general, softwoods are less decorative and tend to be used for structural work, painted joinery and trim. Hardwoods are more often used for decorative work, polished joinery and trim. Timbers readily absorb and lose moisture to achieve a balance with their surroundings. However this causes the timber to expand and shrink, which can cause it to distort, split and crack. In addition damp and wet timber is highly susceptible to fungal decay.

Timber may be either supplied loose in individual lengths, in banded packs, or in shrink-wrapped plastic packs.

Individual lengths should be off-loaded manually; long lengths and large sections may require a person at each end. Banded or wrapped loads are best off-loaded mechanically using either the lorry-mounted device, a fork-lift truck or a crane.

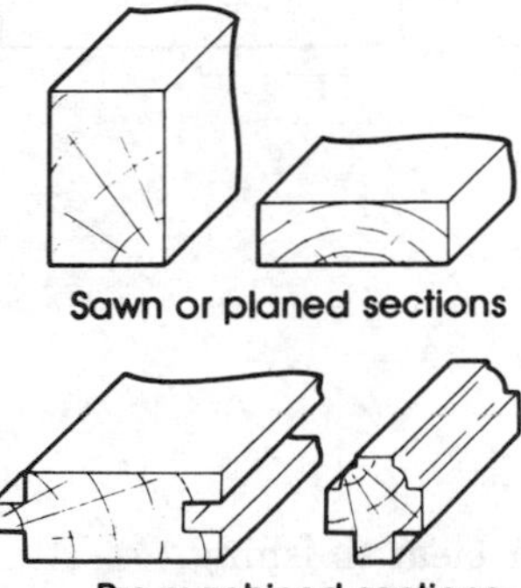

Timber supplied in shrink-wrapped plastic packs should be stored in them until required for use. Care must be taken not to damage the plastic.

Carcassing timber and external joinery should be stored horizontally level to prevent distortion, and clear of the ground on bearers to prevent absorption of ground moisture. Piling sticks or cross-bearers should be placed between each layer, at centres of about 600 mm, to provide support and allow air circulation.

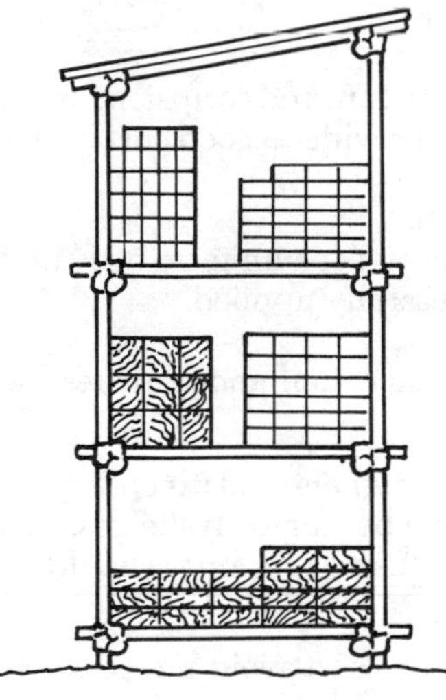

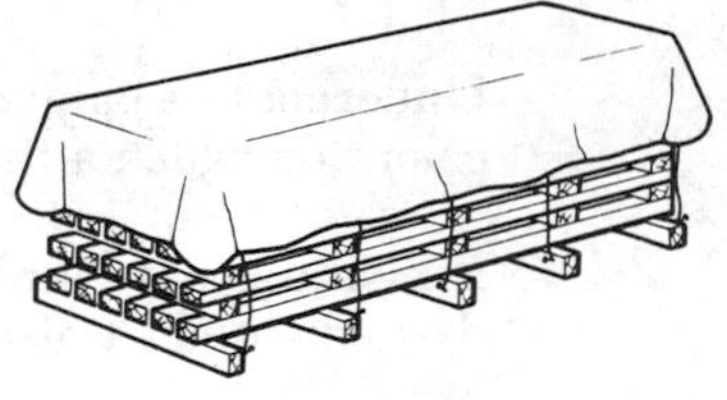

To protect timber against rain, frost, direct sunlight and atmospheric pollution, all stacks should be covered with a tarpaulin or polythene sheets, weighted or tied at the bottom. Care must be taken to allow free air circulation through the stack, to reduce the risk of fungal attack and condensation problems.

Internal trim and other planed sections may be stored horizontally in open-ended covered racks. Priming or sealing of trim and planed sections should be carried out on receipt, if it has not been done prior to delivery.

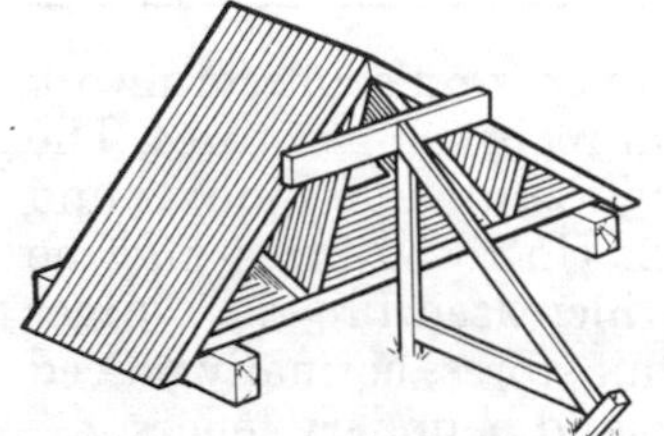

Trussed rafters are either supplied singly or in banded sets. They should be racked upright against a firm support, on eaves bearers. Alternatively, trussed rafters may be stored horizontally on close-spaced bearers, to give level support and prevent deformation. Stacks should be covered with a tarpaulin or polythene sheets, weighted or tied at the bottom. Care must be taken to allow free air circulation through the stack, to reduce the risk of fungal attack, condensation or connector corrosion problems.

Storage of hazardous products

Paint

This is a thin decorative and/or protective coating which is applied in a liquid or plastic form and later dries out or hardens to a solid film covering a surface. Paints consist of a film former, known as the vehicle; a thinner or solvent (water, white spirit or methylated spirit, etc.) to make the coating liquid enough; and a pigment suspended in the vehicle to provide covering power and colour. Paint schemes require either the application by brush, spray or roller, of one or more coats of the same material (varnish, emulsion and solvent paints) or a build up of different successive coats, each having their own functions (primer, undercoat and finishing coat).

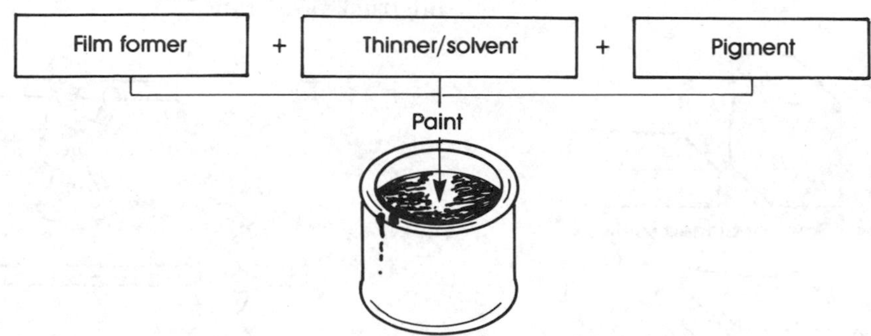

Varnish – a paint without a pigment, used for clear finishing.

Emulsion – a water-thinned paint for use on walls and ceilings.

Solvent paint – based on rubber, bitumen or coal tar and used for protecting metals and water-proofing concrete, etc.

Primer – may form a protective coat against moisture and corrosion, or act as a barrier between dissimilar materials. Also provides a good surface for subsequent coats.

Undercoat – a paint used on primed surfaces to give it a uniform body and colour on which a finishing coat can be successfully applied.

Finishing coat – seals the surface, gives the final colour and provides the desired surface finish (flat, eggshell, gloss).

Paints are mainly supplied in 1, 2.5 and 5 litre containers, and exceptionally in bulk or trade 25 litre containers. These should be stored on shelves, in a secure store, at an even temperature. Each shelf and container should be marked with its contents.

Large containers should be placed on lower shelves to avoid unnecessary lifting.

Highly flammable liquids

White spirit, cellulose, most special paint thinners and some formwork release agents give off a vapour that can burn at room temperatures. The use of these liquids is controlled by the Highly Flammable Liquids and Liquefied Petroleum Gases Regulations, 1972. Up to 50 litres may be stored in a normal store, but because of the increased fire risk, larger quantities must be stored in special fire-resistant stores, normally placed at least 4 m away from buildings, work places and boundary fences.

All storerooms used for hazardous products should be no smoking areas; signs stating 'NO SMOKING – FLAMMABLE' and 'HIGHLY FLAMMABLE SUBSTANCES' must be prominently displayed.

Suitable fire extinguishers must be available to deal with the potential hazard. See *'Health and Safety'*.

Rags used to mop up a spillage must **never** be left in the store. Rolled up dirty rags start to generate heat and can eventually burst into flames (spontaneous combustion). This creates an ignition source for the entire store contents.

Hazardous products may be used directly from their container or a smaller amount decanted into a 'kettle' for convenience. The surplus should be returned to the main container after use. **Never** store any substance in an unlabelled container.

To decant from container to kettle: dust the top of the container; remove the lid with an opener; thoroughly stir the contents with a mixing knife to achieve an even consistency; pour the required quantity into the kettle, from the side opposite the manufacturer's instructions; use a brush to mop up the surplus on the rim or side of the container; scrape the brush on the edge of the kettle to remove surplus; firmly replace the container lid to prevent vapours escaping and dust and dirt getting in.

Consult the manufacturer's instructions on the container prior to decanting as certain substances **must not** be used or stored in another container for reasons of safety (it parts them from their use/safety instructions and renders the contents unknown).

Decanting of hazardous products should be carried out in well-ventilated conditions.

Gases

Liquefied petroleum gas (LPG) sold commercially as propane and butane is supplied in pressurized metal cylinders ranging from 4 kg to 50 kg in size.

Cylinders should be stored upright in a well-ventilated fire-resisting storeroom, or in a secure compound away from any heat source. A minimum of two exits are normally required for an LPG store.

A sign stating 'NO SMOKING, HIGHLY FLAMMABLE SUBSTANCES' should be displayed. Empty and full cylinders should be stored separately and empty ones clearly marked as such.

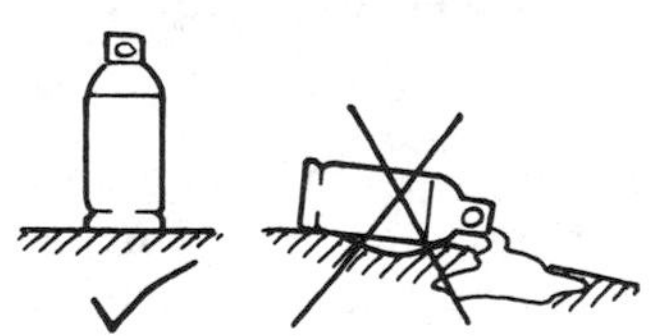

Never use or store cylinders on their sides, near to or in excavations, in confined spaces or in other areas with restricted ventilation.

All valves should be fully closed. LPG is heavier than air and it will collect at low levels where an ignition source (discarded match, sparking power tool, dirty rags) could ignite it.

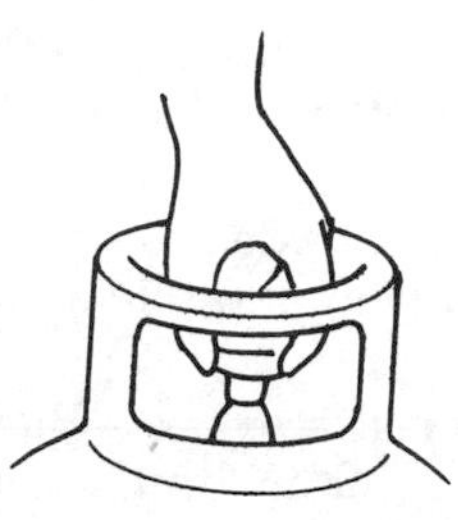

Storage of fragile or perishable materials

Bagged materials

Cement – manufactured from chalk or limestone and clay which are ground into a powder, mixed together and fired in a kiln causing a chemical reaction. On leaving the kiln, the resulting material is ground to a fine powder. Hence a popular site term for cement is 'dust'. When water is added to the cement, another reaction takes place causing it to gradually stiffen, harden and develop strength.

Ordinary Portland cement (OPC) – when hardened its appearance resembles Portland stone.

Rapid hardening Portland cement (RHPC) – for cold weather use.

Sulphate-resisting Portland cement (SRPC) – for use underground in high sulphate conditions.

White or coloured Portland cement – made using white china clay; pigments are added for coloured cements.

High alumina cement (HAC) – uses bauxite (aluminium oxide) instead of clay. It develops very early strength which is much higher than OPC, although in the long term it has been found unstable and thus is now rarely favoured for structural work.

Cement is used in all forms of *in situ* and pre-cast concrete products, cement mortar, cement screeds and rendering.

Plaster – applied on internal walls and ceilings to provide a jointless, smooth, easily decorated surface. External plastering is normally called rendering. Plaster is a mixture that hardens after application; it is based on a binder (gypsum, cement or lime) and water with or without the addition of aggregates. Depending on the background (surface being plastered) plastering schemes may require the application of either one coat, or undercoats to build up a level surface followed by a finishing coat.

Gypsum plaster – for internal use different grades of gypsum plaster are used according to the surface and coat. For undercoats, browning is generally used for brick and blockwork or bonding for concrete; for finishing coats, finish is used on an undercoat or board finish for plasterboard.

Cement–sand plaster – used for external rendering, internal undercoats and water-resisting finishing coats.

Lime–sand plaster – used for both undercoats and (rarely) finishing coats, although lime can be added to other plasters to improve their workability.

Lime – ground, powdered white limestone added to plaster and mortar mixes to improve workability.

Bagged material storage – Bagged materials may be supplied loose in individual bags or in unit loads shrink-wrapped in plastic on timber pallets.

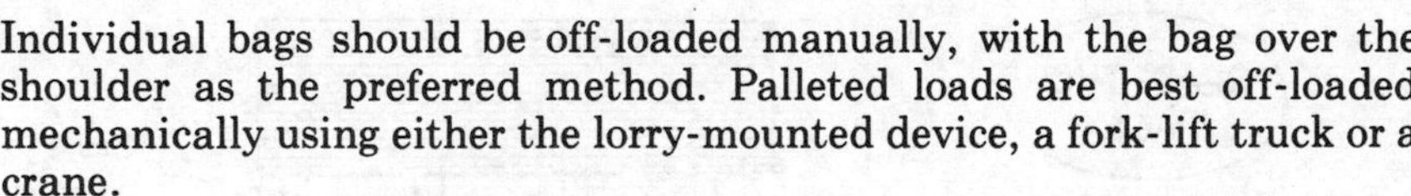

Individual bags should be off-loaded manually, with the bag over the shoulder as the preferred method. Palleted loads are best off-loaded mechanically using either the lorry-mounted device, a fork-lift truck or a crane.

Bags supplied in shrink-wrapped loads are best stored in these until required for use. Care must be taken not to damage the plastic.

Bags should be stored in ventilated, waterproof sheds, on a sound dry floor, with different products having their own shed to avoid confusion.

Bags should be stored clear of the walls and no more than eight to ten bags high. This is to prevent bags becoming damp through a defect in the outside wall, causing the contents to set in the bag. It also reduces the risk of compaction ('warehouse setting') of the lower bags due to the excessive weight of the bags above.

Bags should be used in the same order as they were delivered, known as 'first in, first out'. This is to minimise the storage time and prevent the bag contents becoming stale or 'air setting'.

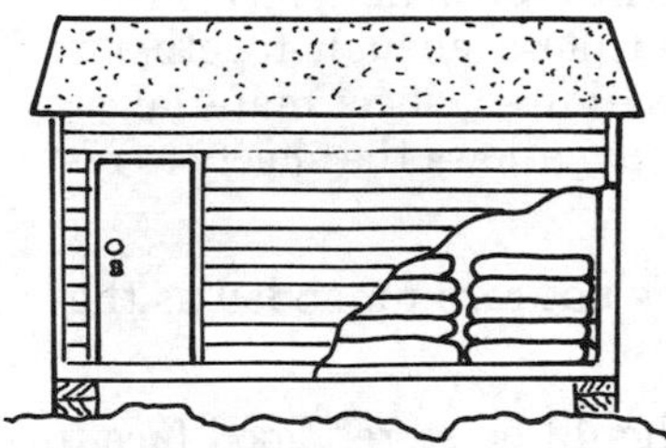

Where small numbers of bags are stored and a shed is not available, they may have to be stored in the open. Stack no more than six to eight bags high on timber pallets and cover with tarpaulins or polythene sheets weighted or tied at ground level.

Sheet materials

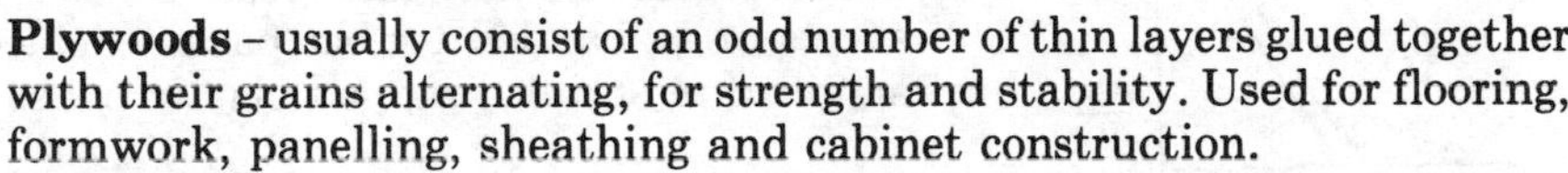

Supplied either as individual sheets, taped face to face in pairs (plasterboard), in banded bundles or unit loads on timber pallets; they may also be supplied in shrink-wrapped plastic packs.

Plywoods – usually consist of an odd number of thin layers glued together with their grains alternating, for strength and stability. Used for flooring, formwork, panelling, sheathing and cabinet construction.

Laminated boards – consist of strips of timber which are glued together, sandwiched between two plywood veneers. They are used for panelling, doors and cabinet construction.

Particle boards – either chipboard (small chips and flakes) or waferboard (large flakes or wafers); both are manufactured using wood chips and/or flakes impregnated with an adhesive. They are used for flooring, furniture and cabinet construction.

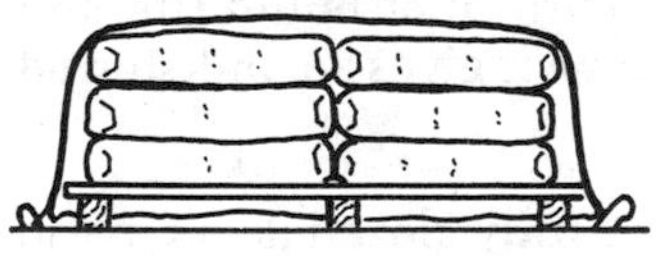

Fibre boards – made from pulped wood, mixed with an adhesive and pressed forming hardboard, medium board, medium density fibre board (MDF) and insulation board. They are used for floor, wall, ceiling and formwork linings, insulation, display boards, furniture and cabinet construction.

Woodwool slabs – made from wood shavings coated with a cement slurry; used for roof decks and as a permanent formwork lining.

Plastic laminate – made from layers of paper impregnated with an adhesive; used for worktops and other horizontal and vertical surfaces requiring decorative hygienic and hard-wearing properties.

Plasterboard – comprises a gypsum plaster core sandwiched between sheets of heavy paper; used for wall and ceiling linings.

Plywood

Blackboard

Laminboard

Particle board (chipboard)

Plasterboard

Individual sheets should be off-loaded manually. To avoid damage they should be carried on edge, which may require a person at each end. Banded

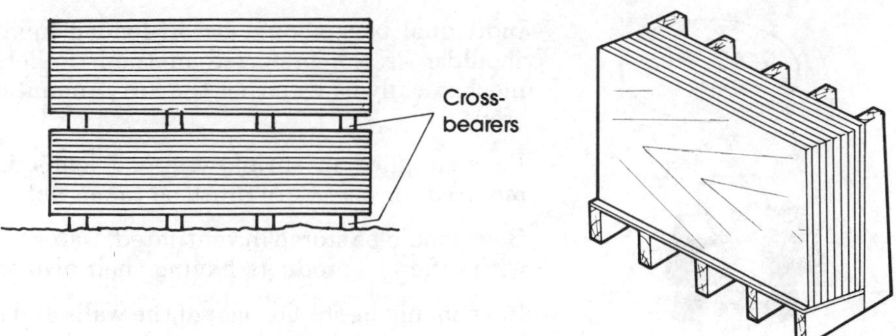

bundles or palleted loads are best off-loaded mechanically using either the lorry-mounted device, a fork-lift truck or a crane.

Sheets supplied in shrink-wrapped plastic packs should be stored in them until required for use. Care must be taken not to damage the plastic.

All sheet materials should preferably be stored in a warm dry place; ideally stacked flat on timber cross-bearers, spaced close enough together to prevent sagging. Alternatively, where space is limited, sheet material can be stored on edge in a purpose-made rack, which allows the sheets to rest against the back board in a true plane.

Leaning sheets against walls on edge or end is not recommended as they will take on a bow which is difficult to reverse.

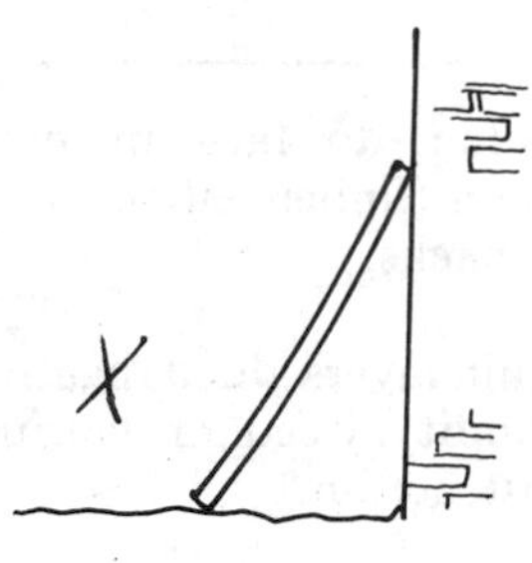

Veneered or other finished surfaced sheets should be stored good face to good face, to minimise the risk of surface scratching.

Glass – a mixture of sand, soda, ash, limestone and dolomite that is heated in a furnace to produce molten glass. On cooling the molten mixture becomes hard and clear. Glass is supplied individually in single sheets or in banded timber packs. Sealed units and cut sizes may be supplied in shrink-wrapped plastic packs for specific purposes.

Drawn glass – molten glass is drawn up between rollers in a continuous flow, cooled in water towers and cut into sheets. Patterned rollers may be introduced to create rough cast and patterned glass. Wire can be incorporated in the glass during the drawing to form wired glass, used for fire-resistant purposes. The surfaces of drawn glass are not perfectly flat, so when you look through your view is distorted. Thus large sheets of glass for shop fronts, etc. have to be ground and polished perfectly flat to give undistorted vision. This type of glass is known as polished plate.

Float glass – molten glass is floated on to the surface of liquid tin, and subsequently allowed to cool. When looked through it gives an undistorted view without the need for polishing.

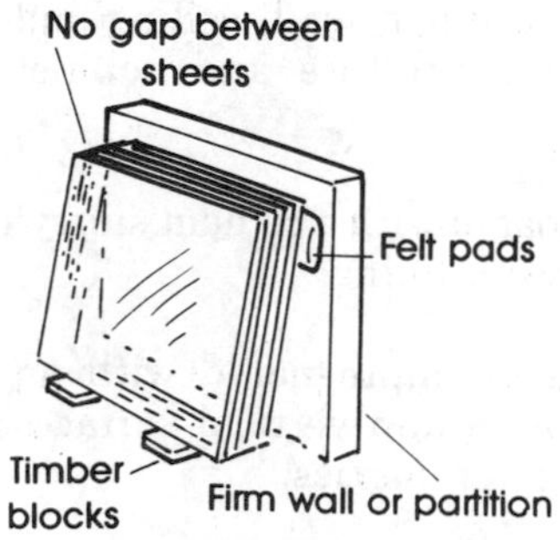

Safety glazing – 'at risk' areas of glazing such as fully glazed doors, patio doors, side panels and other large glazed areas, should contain a safety glazing material. Toughened safety glass is up to five times stronger than standard glass. If broken it will break into fairly small pieces with dulled edges. Laminated safety glass is a sandwich of two or more sheets of glass interlaid with a plastic film. In the event of an impact the plastic holds the sheets of glass together. Depending on the number of layers, impacts from hammer blows and even gun shots can be resisted.

Glass should be stored in dry, wind-free conditions. Never store glass flat as it will distort and break. Sheets should be stood on one long edge almost upright at an angle of about 85 degrees. Timber and/or felt blocks should be used to prevent the glass coming into contact with rough surfaces which can result in scratches or chips. Always stack sheets closely together and never leave spaces, as again this can lead to distortion and subsequent breakage.

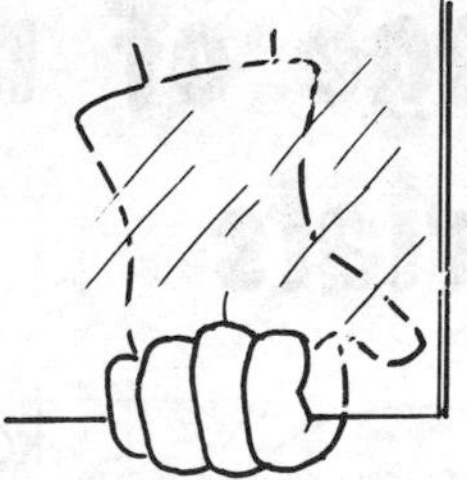

When handling glass use laps to protect your palms. In addition gauntlets may be worn to protect your lower arms and wrists.

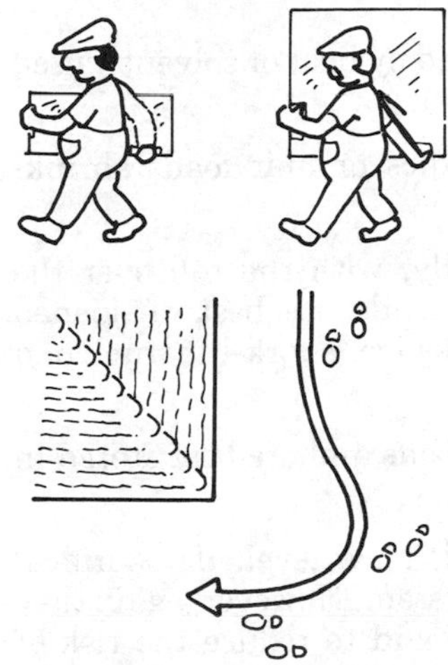

Glass should be held firmly, but not too tightly as it may break. To balance the glass correctly: small panes should be carried under one arm and steadied on the front edge by the other hand; larger panes are held towards your body with one hand under the bottom edge and the other steadying the front; large sheets will require two people to handle them, walking in step, one on each side.

To prevent large panes and sheets 'whipping' when handling it is safer to carry two or more at a time.

Ensure your route is clear of obstructions, keep about a metre out from the wall or building and take a wide path at corners. Do not stop or step back suddenly, since serious injury can be caused by a collision with another person.

If the pane of glass you are carrying breaks or slips, step clear and let it fall freely. Never attempt to catch it.

Vitreous chinaware

Sanitary appliances, such as WC (water closet) pans, WWP (waste water preventer) cisterns, wash basins and shower trays. They are supplied in various ways: as individual items, shrink-wrapped in plastic or with corners taped for protection; in unit loads shrink-wrapped on timber pallets, or increasingly, in bathroom sets including bath, shrink-wrapped on a timber pallet.

Vitreous chinaware – a ceramic material consisting of a mixture of sand and clay which has been shaped, dried and kiln fired, to produce a smooth, hard, glassy surface material. Different colours are achieved by coating items with a prepared glaze solution before firing.

Individual items should be off-loaded manually, with the item firmly gripped with both arms. Palleted loads are best off-loaded mechanically using either the lorry-mounted device, a fork-lift truck or a crane.

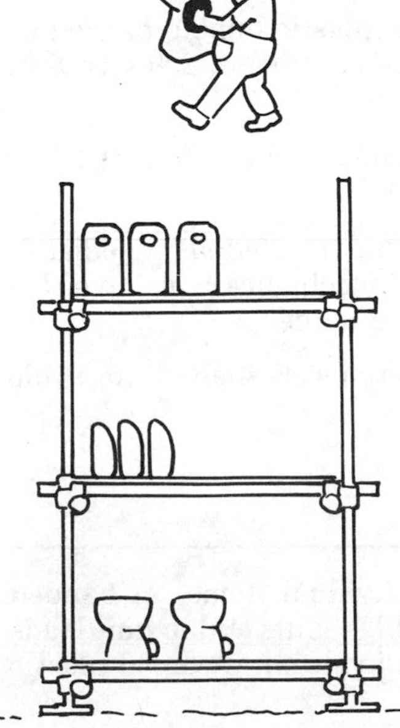

Items are supplied in shrink-wrapped plastic loads and are best stored in them until required for use.

Individual items should be nested together on timber bearers, or alternatively stored in a racking system.

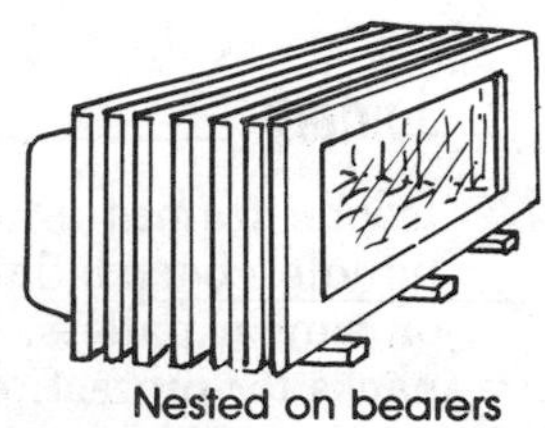
Nested on bearers

Storage of miscellaneous materials

Rolled materials

Bitumen – either occurs naturally or distilled from petroleum, used for roofing felt and damp-proof courses (DPCs).

Metal – mainly non-ferrous (not containing iron) such as copper, lead and zinc. Used for roof coverings, DPCs and flashing.

Plastic – polythene, a thermoplastic (is softened by heat or solvent), used for DPCs and damp-proof membranes (DPMs).

Supplied as individual rolls, in banded bundles or unit loads shrink-wrapped on timber pallets.

Individual rolls should be off-loaded manually, with the roll over the shoulder as the preferred method. Palleted loads are best off-loaded mechanically using either the lorry-mounted device, a fork-lift truck or a crane.

Rolls are supplied in shrink-wrapped plastic loads and are best stored in them until required for use.

All rolls should be stacked vertically on end, on a level, dry surface. Alternatively they may be stored in a racking system. However, again they should be vertical to prevent them rolling off and to reduce the risk of compression damage (e.g. the layers of bitumen rolls melt together under pressure) due to excessive loads (this occurs if rolls are stacked horizontally on top of each other).

Ironmongery

Carpenters' locks, bolts, handles, screws and nails, etc. are 'desirable' items which are most likely to 'walk' unless stored securely under the control of a storeperson.

They are supplied either as individual items, plastic bubble-packed on cards or in boxed sets, by amount, e.g. 10 pairs of hinges, 200 screws or 25 kg of nails, etc.

Large ironmongery deliveries may be supplied in mixed unit loads shrink-wrapped on timber pallets.

Individual items should be off-loaded manually and transferred immediately to the store. Palleted loads are best off-loaded mechanically using either the lorry-mounted device, a fork-lift truck or a crane.

Large or heavy items should be stored on lower shelves to avoid unnecessary lifting.

Joinery

Doors, frames and units are supplied as individual items, in banded bundles, boxed, flat-packed or as ready assembled units and in unit loads on timber pallets. They may also be supplied in shrink-wrapped plastic packs for protection.

Individual joinery items should be off-loaded manually. To avoid damage and stress they should be carried on edge or in their plane of use. This may require a person at each end. Banded bundles or palleted loads are best off-loaded mechanically using either the lorry-mounted device, a fork-lift truck or a crane.

Items supplied in shrink-wrapped packs should be stored in them until required for use. Care must be taken not to damage the plastic.

All joinery items should preferably be stored in a warm dry place; ideally stacked flat to prevent twisting and on timber cross bearers, spaced close enough together to prevent sagging. Also see 'Timber' on page 137.

Leaning items against walls on edge or end is not recommended, as they will take on a bow, rendering them unusable.

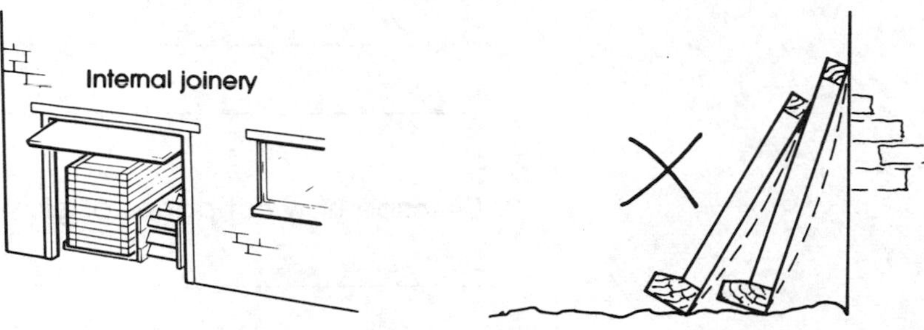

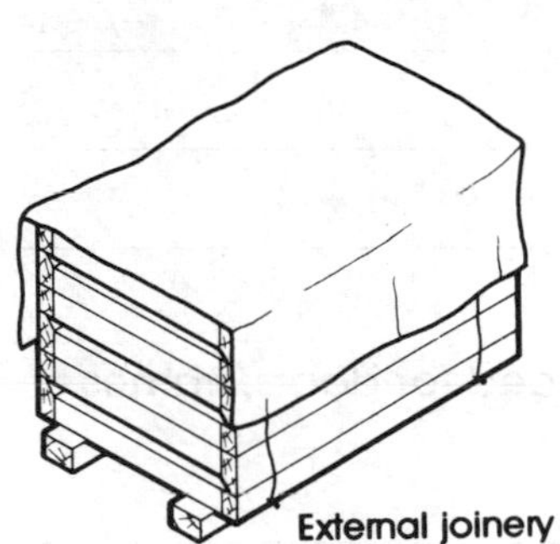

Questions for you

3. Name a bulk building material and state the reason why it should be stored clear of the ground.

4. State the purpose of covering stored building materials.

5. Explain why piling sticks or cross-bearers are used when stacking timber.

6. State why it is not good practice to store liquids in unmarked containers.

7. Explain the term 'first in, first out' when applied to the use of bagged materials.

8. State the reasons why rolled materials are normally stored vertically on end.

9. Describe how cut panes of glass should be stored prior to use.

10. Explain why flat storage is recommended for doors, frames and sheet materials.

11. Name an item of safety clothing used when handling glass.

12. Identify the materials from the following descriptions:
(a) a walling unit component having a standard format size including a 10 mm mortar allowance of 225 mm × 112.5 mm × 75 mm.
(b) a paint used to form a protective coat against moisture and corrosion, or act as a barrier between dissimilar materials.
(c) a sheet material that is formed by being floated on to the surface of liquid tin.

(a) ____________________

(b) ____________________

(c) ____________________

WORD-SQUARE SEARCH

Hidden in the word-square are the following 20 words associated with '*Materials*'. You may find the words written forwards, backwards, up, down or diagonally.

Handling	Aggregate
Security	Bearers
Bricks	Emulsion
Timber	Paint
Protection	Flammable
Tarpaulin	Hazardous
Mortar	Plaster
Banded	Vitreous
Tile	Ironmongery
Lintel	Plasterboard

Draw a ring around the words, or line in using a highlight pen thus:

EXAMPLE

EXAMPLE

H	A	N	D	L	I	N	G	S	V	Y	T	I	R	U	C	E	S
R	U	S	P	I	I	T	B	E	I	P	I	R	R	E	W	O	T
O	R	T	S	N	L	M	R	D	T	L	M	O	R	T	A	R	A
P	I	C	L	T	D	D	I	R	R	A	B	M	B	M	E	O	N
R	A	D	D	E	Y	A	C	E	E	S	E	O	O	U	H	R	D
I	U	H	L	L	G	O	T	G	O	T	R	S	L	N	E	T	A
E	A	N	O	E	P	A	S	U	U	E	R	N	T	N	I	A	P
H	A	Z	A	R	D	O	U	S	S	R	D	A	H	C	M	N	D
A	G	G	R	E	G	A	T	E	I	B	O	R	T	A	E	E	F
R	A	C	O	C	C	D	R	M	R	O	S	T	L	N	T	D	L
P	L	A	S	T	E	R	G	U	A	A	H	O	C	I	S	N	A
U	D	N	E	D	E	G	T	L	S	R	A	E	A	L	T	E	M
R	R	S	N	V	N	D	A	S	C	D	D	B	N	U	P	P	M
O	A	A	V	I	U	S	T	I	M	E	E	O	I	A	C	E	A
L	B	R	C	O	U	P	L	O	R	S	L	A	T	P	O	D	B
K	Y	R	E	G	N	O	M	N	O	R	I	R	O	R	C	N	L
F	R	C	T	A	S	B	M	L	A	D	T	D	E	A	S	I	E
B	E	A	R	E	R	S	D	N	O	I	T	C	E	T	O	R	P

WELL THAT'S IT. SEE YOU IN THE NEXT PACKAGE